Growing Grapes
in Eastern Washington

*Proceedings from the 1998
Washington State University shortcourse
for establishing a vineyard
and producing grapes.*

Growing Grapes
in Eastern Washington

Proceedings from the 1998 Washington State University shortcourse
for establishing a vineyard and producing grapes

Edited by
JOHN (JACK) WATSON

GOOD FRUIT GROWER
Yakima, Washington

First printed August 1999
10 9 8 7 6 5 4 3 2 1

Printed in the United States of America

Library of Congress Cataloging-in-Publication Data
Growing grapes in eastern Washington : proceedings from the 1998 Washington
State University shortcourse for establishing a vineyard and
producing grapes / edited by John (Jack) Watson.
p.   cm.
Includes bibliographical references.
ISBN 0-9630659-8-X
1. Viticulture--Washington (State), Eastern Congresses.
I. Watson, John, 1939-   .
SB387.76.W2G76   1999   99-28543
634.8'09797--dc21   CIP

Good Fruit Grower
105 South 18th Street, Suite 217
Yakima, Washington 98901 U.S.A.
Telephone (800) 487-9946
www.goodfruit.com

Shortcourse Faculty

RON BENITZ
Vineyard Manager
Sagemoor Farms
Pasco, WA

VERNON BROWN
Nurseryman
Fairacres Nursery
Prosser, WA

WYATT CONE
Entomologist
Washington State University Irrigated
Agriculture Research and Extension Center
Prosser, WA

MIKE CONCIENNE
Director of Field Operations
National Grape Cooperative
Grandview, WA

JERRY DECOTO
Viticulturist
Stimson Lane Vineyards and Estates
Paterson, WA

ROBERT EVANS
Agriculture Engineer
Washington State University Irrigated
Agriculture Research and Extension Center
Prosser, WA

RAY FOLWELL
Agriculture Economist
Washington State University
Pullman, WA

GARY GROVE
Plant Pathologist
Washington State University Tree Fruit
Research and Extension Center
Wenatchee, WA

GORDON HILL
Winemaker
Columbia Crest Winery
Grandview, WA

KEITH MARTIN
Grower Relations
Valley Processing
Sunnyside, WA

MIKE MEANS
Pest Management Specialist
Stimson Lane Vineyards and Estates
Paterson, WA

BILL POWERS
Badger Mountain Vineyard
and Powers Winery
Kennewick, WA

TONY RYNDERS
Winemaker
Hogue Cellars
Prosser, WA

RAY SANDIDGE
Winemaker
Kestrel Winery
Prosser, WA

STEVE SENSNEY
U.S. Bank
Grandview, WA

SARA SPAYD
Food Scientist
Washington State University Irrigated
Agriculture Research and Extension Center
Prosser, WA

ROBERT STEVENS
Soil Scientist
Washington State University Irrigated
Agriculture Research and Extension Center
Prosser, WA

ROBERT WAMPLE
Horticulturist
Washington State University Irrigated
Agriculture Research and Extension Center
Prosser, WA

TOM WALISER
Grower
Walla Walla, WA

JOHN (JACK) WATSON
Washington State University
Cooperative Extension
Prosser, WA

WADE WOLFE
Viticulturist, Winemaker
Hogue Cellars/
Thurston Wolfe Winery
Prosser, WA

Foreword

Wine and juice grape production in eastern Washington State has increased rapidly in recent years. The high quality of the grapes grown under eastern Washington's conditions are producing world class wine and high quality juice. Demand for these products is outstripping production, and wineries and processors have been encouraging growers to plant more grapes. In addition, because of low returns for apples and other agricultural commodities, growers are looking for alternative crops to replace unprofitable ones.

The 1998 Washington State University Shortcourse Growing Grapes in Eastern Washington was developed to supply the informational needs of growers interested in producing wine and juice grapes. It also was intended for established growers interested in obtaining current information on grape production in our unique growing area.

These proceedings from the shortcourse will help potential growers to evaluate the economics and feasibility of a vineyard enterprise and provide growers with a guide to the production practices necessary to establish and produce grapes.

Tribute must be paid to the shortcourse faculty for preparing and presenting the information. Thanks also are extended to Rama Tramel and Linda Watson for their help at registration and to the *Good Fruit Grower* for taking a chance and publishing this effort.

John (Jack) Watson

Table of Contents

The Economic Realities of Growing Grapes in Eastern Washington

RAYMOND J. FOLWELL
Department of Agricultural Economics
Washington State University

I nterest in grape growing in eastern Washington has once again reached a peak. In 1997, the Concord grape industry experienced record high prices with the second largest crop ever harvested. The wine grape industry also harvested a large crop which was equal to the 1993 record crop and still received the second highest prices ever paid for wine grapes. This chapter will review the basic economic conditions surrounding each of these industries, as well as the costs of establishing and operating vineyards. In addition, cost information on establishing and operating wineries of various sizes is summarized.

CONCORD GRAPES

Washington leads among U.S. states in Concord grape production. All indications are that the production (planted area) will continue

---

FIGURE I

Washington Concord grape production, 1979-1997.

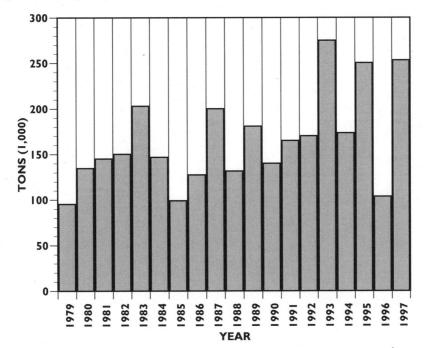

FIGURE 2

Production and yield of Concord grapes, 1969-1997.

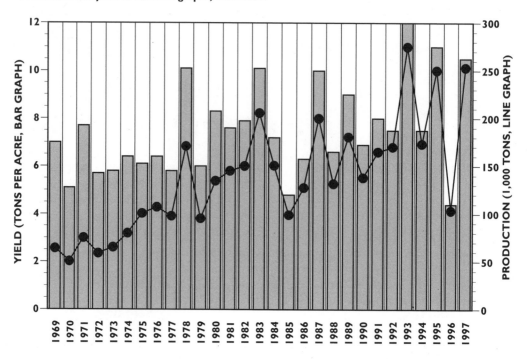

FIGURE 3

Washington Concord grape prices, 1979-1997 (cash prices for 16° Brix grapes).

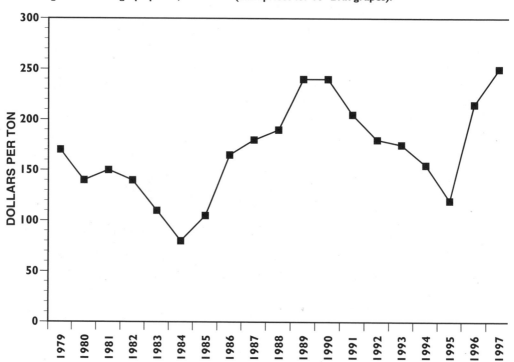

to increase in Washington relative to the eastern producing states.

The 1997 Washington Concord grape harvest was 255,514.7 tons *(Figure 1),* the second largest Concord grape crop harvested in Washington. This is up from the 103,521-ton crop in 1996. The all-time record crop of 275,000 tons was in 1993.

There has been a general trend of increasing crop size since 1985, with the exception of 1996. The 1996 and 1997 seasons emphasize the importance of reminding growers that the interaction of weather with cultural practices determines the yield per acre and resulting crop size of Concord grapes in Washington.

Concord grape vineyards yielded an average of slightly more than ten tons per acre in 1997. The size of this 1997 crop and lateness of that harvest could limit production in 1998.

Under such conditions, one would expect some vineyards not to obtain the degree of winter hardiness desired nor to have stored the most desirable level of carbohydrates. However, all indications by spring 1998 are that the crop will again be above average.

There have not been any significant plantings of Concord grapes in the last few years. Therefore, the yield per acre and total tonnage harvested are highly related *(Figure 2).* There is some new interest in planting Concord grape vineyards. New plantings may start to occur in the near future as a result of the high price in 1997.

The 1997 crop was accompanied by a significant increase in the base price for 16° Brix Concord grapes to $250 per ton *(Figure 3).* This is $35 per ton higher than the 1996 price and $10 higher than the previous record price of $240 per ton in 1989 and 1990.

Overall, the expected inverse relationship between the quantity supplied and price did not exist in 1997 *(Figure 4).* The price was higher because of the improved demand situation, the extremely short crop in 1996, and the extremely low inventories.

The eastern Concord grape production areas had problems in 1997. The harvest in New York was only two-thirds of that in 1996. The production was below normal in the other eastern producing states but was not

FIGURE 4

Washington Concord grape prices and production, 1979-1997 (prices for 16° Brix grapes).

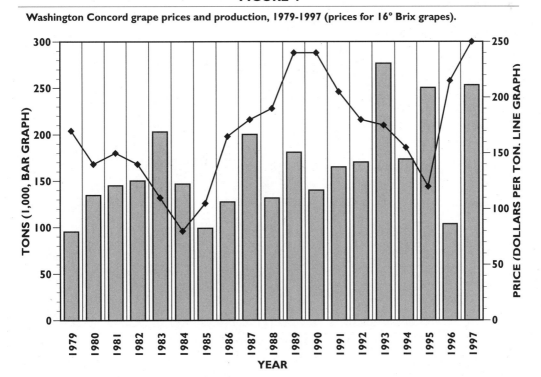

FIGURE 5

Concord grape production in Washington, New York, and the U.S. total, 1983-1997.

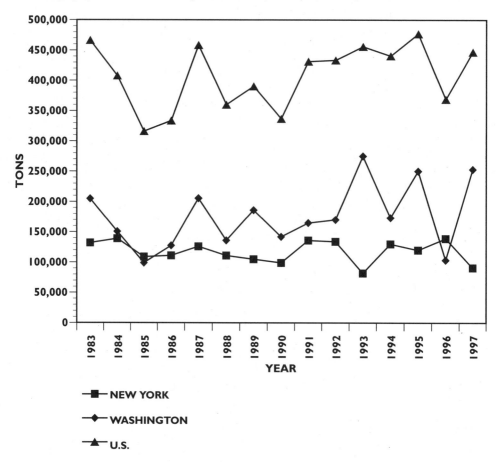

FIGURE 6

Concord grape acreage in Washington, 1968-1997.

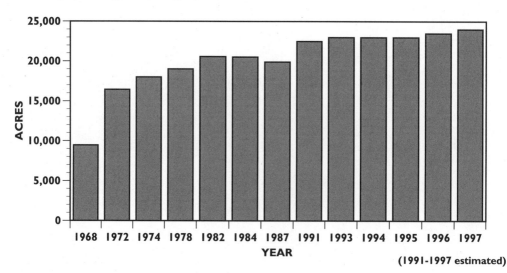

(1991-1997 estimated)

down as much. Pennsylvania had only three-quarters of the crop harvested in 1996, Ohio about 90%, while Michigan was down only slightly. The berry size in the eastern producing areas was small.

With New York and the other Concord grape-producing areas experiencing below normal crops and Washington having a 150,000-ton increase in its production, the overall supply of Concord grapes in the United States was up at the end of the 1997 harvest *(Figure 5)*. The total supply of Concord grapes from 1997 harvest in the United States was about 447,000 tons, as compared to crops of over 400,000 tons annually since 1990. The only exception was in 1996. The supply in 1996 was the smallest since 1988, which partially explains why the cash price was higher in 1997.

As a result of the supply situation, the concentrate price in the East is $16.00 per gallon and ranged from $13.90 to $16.00 per gallon in the West at the time of harvest. This translates into an equivalent farm price of $511 to $589 per ton without accounting for any processing, inventory, marketing, or distribution costs. The market prices soften to $12.00 to $12.50 per gallon by April.

The Concord grape acreage has been relatively stable *(Figure 6)*. Today, it stands at 24,000 acres. There have been some Concord grape vineyards removed, but the recent plantings have offset the removals. There will be additional new plantings, given the record 1997 price.

Cost of Establishing and Operating a Concord Grape Vineyard

Extension Bulletin EB1823 was used as a basis to estimate the 1998 costs of establishing and operating a Concord grape vineyard. The EB1823 information was adjusted to 1998 by using the index of prices paid by farmers for all production inputs. As a result, the costs reported herein are based upon the same assumptions as used in EB1823.

WINE GRAPES
Economic Trends

The 1997 wine grape crop in Washington followed the same roller coaster trend as the Concord grape production. The 1997 wine grape crop was 62,000 tons *(Figure 7)*. This was almost double the 35,000 tons harvested in 1996.

FIGURE 7

Production of wine grapes in Washington (1977-1997).

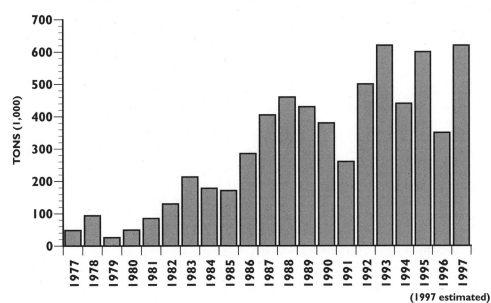

(1997 estimated)

TABLE 1

Summary of net investment costs (1998) in establishing a 30-acre Concord grape vineyard ($/acre).

Cost Category	Establishment Years				Total Establishment Cost
	First	Second	Third	Fourth	
Receipts:					
Yields(tons)	0	0	3	6	
Price ($/ton)	$180	$180	$180	$180	
Revenue	0	0	540	1,080	$1,620
Variable Costs:					
Preharvest	1,370	2,862	325	320	4,877
Harvest	0	0	127	254	381
Postharvest	0	0	247	247	494
Total Variable Costs	1,370	2,862	699	821	5,752
Fixed Costs:					
Trac/Pickup/4WHL	205	255	121	126	707
Machinery	19	36	26	27	108
Irrigation	228	228	228	228	912
Net Land Rent	130	130	130	130	520
Real Estate Tax	33	62	62	75	232
Interest on Accumulated Investment	---	201	584	715	1,500
Total Fixed Costs	615	912	1,151	1,301	3,979
Total Costs	1,985	3,774	1,850	2,122	9,731
Net Investment Costs	$1,985	$3,774	$1,310	$1,042	$8,111

The quality of the wine grape crop was good overall. Naturally there were some exceptions to this statement. The premium white and most of the red varieties had good fruit characteristics. This should contribute to continued production of high quality premium table wines for which Washington is noted.

The average price for all wine grape varieties was $972 per ton in 1997 *(Figure 8)*. The red or black varieties were approximately $1,255 per ton, while the white varieties were about $784 per ton. In 1996, the average price for all varieties was $948 per ton. The red varieties averaged $1,260 per ton. The slight decrease, in spite of the larger crop, was a direct reflection of the demand that exists for wine grapes at the winery level given the short 1996 crop. These prices are the second highest experienced during the short history of the Washington wine industry.

The demand for Washington wines continues to expand *(Figure 9)*. Washington wine sales were up 11% in the time period July 1, 1995, through June 30, 1996. The sales of

TABLE 2

Estimated revenues and costs of production (1998) on a 30-acre Concord grape vineyard ($/acre).

Revenue and Cost Category	Amount
Revenue:	
Yield	8.0 Tons
Price/Ton	$180
Total Revenue/Acre	$1,440
Variable Costs:	
Nonharvest	$339
Harvest	$619
Total Variable Costs	$958
Fixed Costs:	
Irrigation Equipment	$228
Tractor and Machine	$172
Real Estate Tax	$75
Interest on Investment	$961
Net Land Rent	$130
Total Fixed Costs	$1,566
Total Costs	$2,524
Profit/Loss	($1,084)

Washington wine will show some decline when the statistics are released. This is similar to the situation in 1992 after the short wine grape crop in 1991. Some wineries did not have enough product to satisfy all demands and had to put some wines on allocation.

Wine sales in the United States increased in 1996, as compared to 1995 *(Figure 10)*.

This is the third straight year since the mid 1980s that wine sales have increased. Total wine sales were up 8.3%. The category of U.S.-produced wine increased 5.54% with U.S.-produced table wines increasing 5.51%. All the other types of U.S.-produced wines experienced a slight increase in sales, except for sparkling wines. Imported table wines were

TABLE 3

Revenues, yields, and prices used in estimating 1998 costs of establishment, by variety.

Variety	Year				
	1	2	3	4	Full Production
Prices ($/ton)					
Chardonnay	700	700	700	700	700
Merlot	850	850	850	850	850
Yields (tons/acre)					
Chardonnay	0	0	2.5	5.0	6.5
Merlot	0	0	2.5	4.0	5.5
Revenues ($/acre)					
Chardonnay	0	0	1,750	3,500	4,550
Merlot	0	0	2,125	3,400	4,675

FIGURE 8

Production and prices of wine grapes in Washington, 1977-1997.

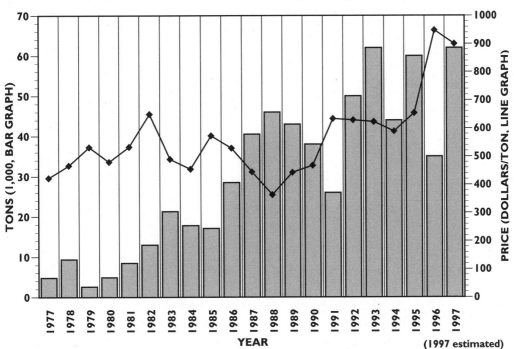

(1997 estimated)

up 25.9%, and the only category of imported wines that had reduced sales in 1996 as compared to 1995 was that which included wine coolers, cider, some bag-in-the-box, and other mixed wines.

Table wines accounted for 79.1% of all wine consumed in the United States. In 1986, table wines accounted for only 62% of the U.S. wine market. Coupled with the increasing popularity of table wines, the per capita consumption of all wine increased. This is only the fourth year out of the last 11 years in which the per capita consumption of wine in the United States increased.

Wine grape acreage in Washington has increased *(Figure 11)*. The plantings during the last two years amounted to 3,502 acres. The total now stands at 16,540 acres, which is 30% more than in 1994. The greatest acreage was planted to Merlot (1,189.5 acres), Chardonnay (1,148.8 acres), and Cabernet Sauvignon (565.1 acres). These three varieties account for 82.9% of the acreage planted in 1996 and 1997.

Washington has not been alone in the planting of these varieties *(Figures 12, 13, and 14)*. In California, there are 82,330 acres of Chardonnay planted, of which 24% is non-bearing; 40,457 acres of Cabernet Sauvignon, of which 18% is nonbearing; and 32,883 acres of Merlot, of which 55% is nonbearing. In addition, 42% of the vineyards in the San Joaquin Valley are not bearing, and 17.6% of the wine grape acreage in Napa, Sonoma, and the Central Coast are not bearing. There is going to be a large supply of wine grapes in a couple of years.

In Washington, the total acreage of 16,540 acres could produce 15,878,400 gallons of wine, based upon an average yield of six tons per acre and 160 gallons per ton. There should be a need for more wineries and cooperage.

Costs of Establishing and Operating a Wine Grape Vineyard

WSU Extension Bulletin EB1588 was used as a basis to estimate the costs of establishing and operating a wine grape vineyard in 1998. The cost data in EB1588 was updated to 1998 by using the index of prices paid by farmers for all inputs. As a result, the 1998 cost estimates are based on the same assumptions as used in EB1588. The cost estimates were only made for Merlot and Chardonnay.

TABLE 4

Estimated 1998 costs of establishment by year for Chardonnay and Merlot ($/acre).

	Year	Variable Costs	Fixed Costs	Total Costs
Chardonnay				
	1	$1,900	$ 491	$2,391
	2	2,591	707	3,298
	3	1,614	1,012	2,626
	4	1,544	1,037	2,581
Merlot				
	1	$1,910	$ 491	$2,401
	2	2,601	707	3,308
	3	1,624	1,013	2,637
	4	1,488	1,004	2,492

TABLE 5

Estimated 1998 annual revenues, costs, and profitability per acre for Chardonnay and Merlot in an established vineyard.

	Total Revenues	Total Costs	Profit (Loss)
Chardonnay	$4,550	$2,638	$1,912
Merlot	$3,675	$2,548	$2,127

FIGURE 9

Annual growth rates of all table wines compared with Washington wines.

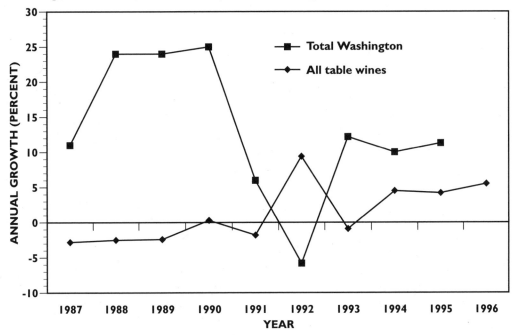

FIGURE 10

Annual growth rates of U.S.-produced wines, 1987-1996.

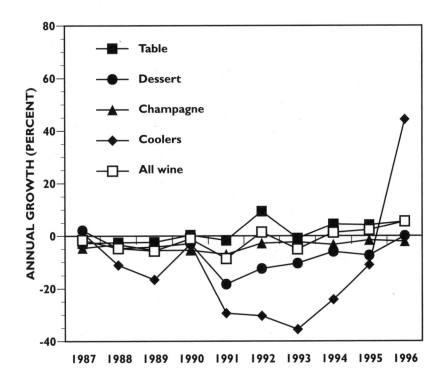

The prices, yields, and total revenues by variety used to estimate the 1998 costs are presented in Table 3. The costs per acre during each of the establishment years are reported in Table 4. If the revenues during the third and fourth years are subtracted from the total costs by year, the net investment costs per acre for the establishment of a Chardonnay vineyard are estimated to be $5,646 per acre and $5,313 per acre for a Merlot vineyard.

Established vineyard revenues, costs, and profits are reported in Table 5. In each case, there is a profit per acre based upon the assumptions used.

Economics of Establishing and Operating a Winery

The investment and operating costs presented in this section are preliminary and based upon ongoing research. The costs are

FIGURE 11

Wine grape acreage in Washington, 1997, by variety.

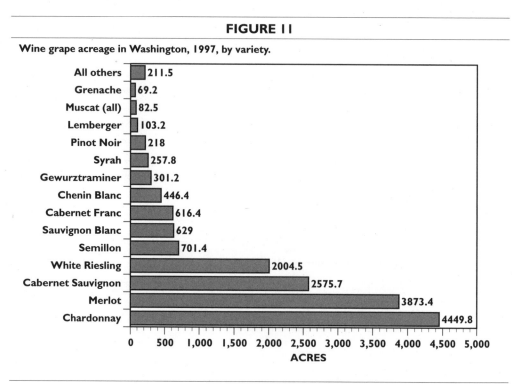

FIGURE 12

Bearing and nonbearing acreage of Chardonnay in Washington (1997) and California (1996).

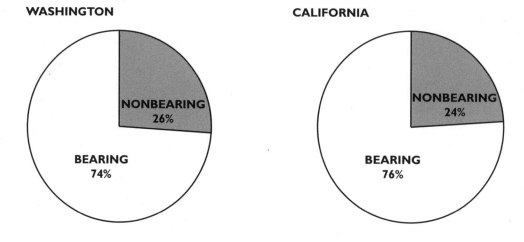

based on numerous assumptions. Details will be forthcoming in WSU bulletins. The costs were estimated for 2,000-, 5,000-, 10,000-, 50,000-, 200,000-, and 500,000-case wineries. The investment costs by major categories of equipment, and plant and office are reported in Table 6. The estimated investment costs range from $451,170 for the 2,000-case winery to $26,225,720 for the 500,000-case winery.

Table 7 contains the estimated cost per case. The costs per case decrease from $82.87 per case for the 2,000-case winery to $39.67 for the 500,000-case winery. There are economies of size.

Table 7 also contains the estimated revenues and costs during the tenth year of operation for each size of winery. These were taken from a detailed cost flow analysis for each size winery. As demonstrated in Table 7, the net cost flows are positive during the tenth year for each size of winery.

However, under the assumptions used, only the wineries of 50,000 cases or fewer are good investments, given the net present values and internal rates of return based upon the assumptions used.

(See Figures 13 and 14 on following page.)

TABLE 6

Investment costs in various sizes of wineries ($).

Winery Size (cases)	Equipment					Plant and Office	Total
	Receiving	Cellars	Refrigeration	Bottling	Material Handling/ Fermentation/ Storage/ Cooperage		
2,000	$ 39,320	$ 33,592	$ 20,000	$ 25,000	$ 154,068	$ 188,190	$ 451,170
5,000	31,800	39,762	37,500	120,000	272,642	225,640	727,344
10,000	64,825	60,950	60,000	120,000	519,148	368,925	1,193,848
50,000	180,940	119,430	75,000	250,000	1,809,699	1,234,560	3,669,629
200,000	340,560	300,970	150,000	420,000	5,782,170	5,120,500	12,114,200
500,000	652,830	596,860	285,000	940,000	12,536,030	11,215,000	26,225,720

TABLE 7

Tenth year total revenues, costs, cash flows, and costs per case by winery size ($).

	Winery Size (cases)					
	2,000	5,000	10,000	50,000	200,000	500,000
Total Revenue	$399,261	$850,722	$1,080,352	$4,305,752	$12,273,740	$28,903,336
Direct Operating Costs	144,450	299,758	530,947	2,117,882	7,818,930	18,462,914
Total Fixed Costs	21,299	29,552	49,192	165,870	648,108	1,373,520
Total Costs	165,749	329,310	580,139	2,283,752	8,467,038	19,836,434
Net Cash Flow	158,072	362,713	328,256	1,329,366	2,496,173	5,948,687
Cost per Case	82.87	65.86	58.01	45.68	42.34	39.67

FIGURE 13

Bearing and nonbearing acreage of Cabernet Sauvignon in Washington (1997) and California (1996).

WASHINGTON

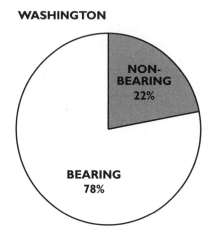

CALIFORNIA

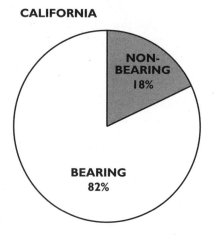

FIGURE 14

Bearing and nonbearing acreage of Merlot in Washington (1997) and California (1996).

WASHINGTON

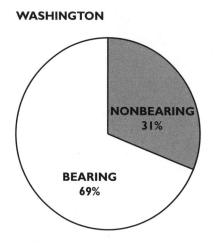

CALIFORNIA

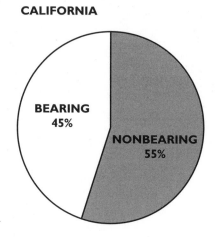

Washington Viticulture– The Basics

JOHN (JACK) WATSON
Washington State University
Area Extension Horticulturist
Prosser, Washington

O ver the past five decades, eastern Washington has proven itself as one of the premier grape-growing areas in the world. Our experience has also shown that the limiting factor for producing a consistent, high quality grape crop is cold injury (U.S. Department of Commerce, 1975).

Many cultural practices take this limitation into consideration. The following sections are devoted to basic commercial viticulture practices employed in eastern Washington, with special attention applied to avoiding cold injury.

CLIMATE

In eastern Washington, there are three primary criteria applied to determine the suitability of climate for grape production. The first of these is the length of growing season (*Figure 1*). At this latitude, 45° to 48°, midseason ripening grapes require 130 to 170 days to mature. Additional time is required after harvest for vines to achieve dormancy. Should a killing frost occur in the spring, fruit buds could be lost and the crop reduced. Frost occurring in the fall before vines go dormant curtails photosynthesis and the

FIGURE I

Mean length of growing season (days above 32°F). Data 1964–1973, Washington.

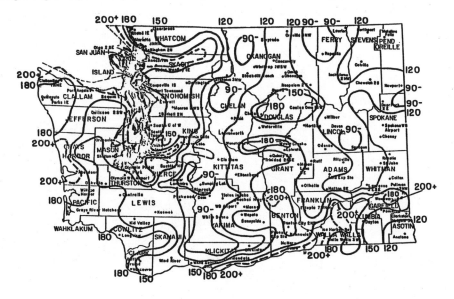

natural dormancy process, making vines more susceptible to winter injury.

The second criterion is the accumulation of heat throughout the growing season *(Figure 2)*. This heat summation, expressed as degree days, is measured by taking the average of the maximum and minimum daily temperature in degrees Fahrenheit and subtracting 50 degrees. Daily heat units are added throughout the growing season to obtain a total for the year. Total heat units should be in excess of 1700 to allow grapes to ripen (Winkler, A.J., 1974). If accumulated heat units exceed 3,500, grapes tend to be low in acid, and quality can suffer.

The third criterion is severely cold winter temperatures *(Figure 3)*. Well-hardened grapevines can usually withstand temperatures around 0°F without injury. At temperatures below -10°F, bud and wood loss can be expected. Should warm temperatures occur just before a severe cold period, vines are dehardened by the warmer weather and become more vulnerable to cold injury. One of the more severe wood losses, particularly on the southwest side of trunks, occurs when direct or snow-reflected sunlight warms grape trunks during cold spells. When the sun sets, temperatures drop rapidly, and trunk tissue becomes very susceptible to cold damage.

Even though eastern Washington's climate can cause cold injury to vines, it provides favorable conditions to grow high quality grapes. Warm, sunny days and cool nights characterize the growing season and provide an excellent balance to grape sugar and acid. Arid conditions reduce disease problems associated with high rainfall and high humidity. And, finally, because of the extreme northern latitude of the eastern Washington grape growing areas, summer days are long and can compensate for the shorter growing season and low heat units.

VARIETIES

There are two species of grapes that are commercially important in Washington. *Vitis labrusca*, grown primarily for juice and jellies, is planted on approximately 24,000 acres in Washington. The varieties of importance are Concord and Niagara. These grapes are native to the eastern coast of the United States and are somewhat more cold hardy than *V. vinifera* varieties. *V. labrusca* vines can be characterized by their trailing habit of growth; leaves that are felty or covered with fine hairs on the lower surface; and by grapes whose skin slips or does not adhere firmly to the pulp. *Labrusca* grapes also differ from other species by their flavor, described as foxy or having a typically Concord-like taste. Concord and Niagara grapes have experienced a period of expansion in the past four

---

FIGURE 2

Heat units (units of 100, based on 50°F, April 1–October 31). Data 1964–1973, Washington.

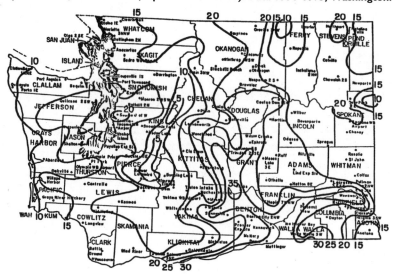

to five years but now seem to be in equilibrium with the market.

Vitis vinifera, the second most important species of grapes in Washington, is grown primarily for wine production. There are about 16,000 acres planted to wine grapes and that industry is currently experiencing strong growth. Varieties of *V. vinifera* are listed in Table 1 (Folwell, R.J., 1998). Small acreages of Nebbiolo, Sangiovese, Viognier, and Pinot Gris are also planted.

French hybrid wine grapes as well as *V. vinifera* table grapes have been grown successfully in eastern Washington, but marketing of these varieties has been difficult.

SITE SELECTION

The suitability of a site for planting grapes is influenced by several factors of climate, soil, and resource availability. The climate should be studied both for its regional influence on heat accumulation, length of growing season, and severe winter temperatures, and as it is affected by site characteristics such as slope, or aspect of the land *(Figure 4)*, wind currents, soil texture, and altitude (Ahmedullah, M., 1985.) Because there is such a strong emphasis on wine grape quality as affected by growing conditions and because of the grape's relative cold intolerance, site selection for *V. vinifera* in eastern Washington is critical. Site selection is more flexible for the more

TABLE 1

Major Washington *Vitis vinifera* varieties and average acreage, 1997.

Red Varieties	Acreage	White Varieties	Acreage
Merlot	3,873	Chardonnay	445
Cabernet Sauvignon	2,576	White Riesling	2,005
Pinot Noir	218	Chenin Blanc	446
Lemberger	103	Sauvignon Blanc	629
Cabernet Franc	616	Semillon	701
Syrah	258	Gewurztraminer	301
		Muscat	83

FIGURE 3

Extreme minimum temperature (°F) 10-year return data up to 1965, Washington.

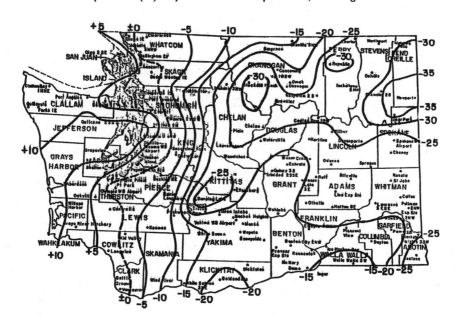

cold tolerant *V. labrusca* but is still an important consideration. Characteristics that are associated with good grape-growing locations include a southern slope with good cold air drainage, less than 1,500 feet in altitude, and light or coarsely textured soil.

Other considerations which may enhance a location would be its close proximity to a large body of water or large rock formation, which can absorb heat and help temper climate in the immediate vicinity. Windy locations tend to have less frost, but strong persistent winds can reduce vine growth and yield. Considerations for selecting a site should also be given to the availability of water, supplies, labor, processing capability, and market access.

NURSERY STOCK

Grape vines are long lived and can be commercially productive for 50 years or more. This fact makes selection of the very best nursery stock to plant a vineyard of utmost importance. By purchasing certified nursery stock, you can guarantee that vines are true to type and have been tested for specific insects, diseases, and viruses.

The next best choice would be to buy young vines that are only one or two generations removed from a certified block. Under no circumstance should uncertified nursery material be brought into the state from other growing areas. This is not only illegal but puts our industry at risk of being infested by viruses or, even worse, phylloxera.

One-year-old rooted hardwood cuttings are best for planting under eastern Washington conditions. To be classified as #1, vines should exhibit good root and shoot growth. Cuttings should be 12 to 18 inches long so that roots can be planted below the soil frost zone.

Rooted hardwood cuttings are dug from nursery rows in the fall after growing for one season and stored for the winter to prevent cold injury. They should be planted in late February or March after the ground thaws and the chance of severely cold temperatures has passed. Fall planting has been used in Washington, but the chance of winter injury makes it a high-risk option. Unrooted, dormant cuttings have been used to establish vineyards, but this practice has inevitably resulted in a reduced stand and poor, nonuniform growth. Unless properly handled, greenhouse cuttings should be avoided because their shallow roots and lack of hardiness make them susceptible to cold injury.

PLANTING

Before planting, the site should be tested for soil depth, fertility, soil compaction, and, if necessary, pesticide residues that may inhibit vine growth. If the site must be leveled, it is best to remove the top soil, level the ground, and then replace the top soil. If there are compaction layers or impermeable soil layers caused by soil minerals, then the soil should be ripped. This is usually done in both directions. Preplant fertilizer should then be incorporated into the soil.

There are several methods of preparing a hole to plant the vine. The most common one is with an auger. There has been increasing interest in hydro-planting or digging the hole with a high powered stream of water. This usually requires that nursery stock roots be severely trimmed to fit into the small diameter of the water-drilled hole.

Research has shown that the more roots retained at planting, the better the subsequent growth will be after planting. This means though hydro-planting is fast, it may not be conducive to rapid first-year growth. Caution should be taken to not glaze the side of the hole if it is dug in wet soil, particularly when using an auger. The smooth sides of the hole make it difficult for roots to penetrate.

When planting, roots should be 10 to 12 inches below the soil surface to avoid cold injury. If the cuttings are relatively short, they should still be planted to twelve inches. However, only partially refill the hole to allow for growing points to remain above the soil line. Once growth is above the ground surface, the hole can be filled. Roots should be spread out and the soil tamped down around them to eliminate air pockets. Plants should be watered at the time of planting.

North-south rows are best for sunlight exposure; however, the topography of the site may be such that a different orientation would be better to help with cold air drainage or irrigation.

Year One

An irrigation system should be installed before or at the time of planting. Vines are pruned after planting to leave two to three buds. This reduces the number of growing points so that shoots that do grow from these buds, grow vigorously. This pruning also helps balance the aboveground portion of the vine with a root system reduced by transplanting.

It is common practice to allow vines to grow without any training the first year. If vines are vigorous and growing conditions are good, some intensive training could establish the vines on the trellis the first year. Because of lack of uniformity and the initial importance of establishing the vine, first-year training is seldom cost effective.

Year Two

At the end of the first year, vines are hilled for winter protection. The trellis is usually installed during the first dormant season. In early spring after the first dormant season, vines are again pruned back to two to three buds. One, or preferably two, trunks are then trained to the trellis wire. Grow tubes can be helpful during this period. These are plastic or cardboard tubes placed around the vine. They create a small greenhouse for the plant and can increase growth up to 30%. They also direct vine growth, which can eliminate several training steps. Contact herbicides can be sprayed near the vines with grow tubes around them without getting material on the leaves. When string is used in training, never tie it to the trunk below the desired growing points.

If the vine has two trunks, they are trained in opposite directions along the wire when they reach it. If only one trunk is used, it is cut at the wire, and the two shoots emerging from the topmost buds are trained in opposite directions along the wire. Never tightly wrap shoots around cordon wires. Vines are usually pruned as late as possible in the spring. When establishing vines on the wire, only five to six buds should be left on each side of the trunk. This insures that the vine will not be overcropped and that all buds, which will become permanent fruiting positions, remain viable and vigorous. Canes are then extended out the third year to establish the permanent arms or cordons.

TRAINING AND PRUNING

The goal of growers the first two years is to establish strong uniform vines onto the trellis wire to begin producing a limited amount of fruit in the third year. Shortcuts in pruning and training usually result in lack of uniformity or premature production of fruit, which may permanently affect future vine productivity.

For most trellis systems, training steps are the same for the first three years. During the first year, vines are usually allowed to grow on the ground. Little or no pruning or training is employed. Young vines can be hilled over with soil or mulch the first winter to help protect them if the winter is severely cold. The trellis is installed at the end of the first year during the dormant season. In the spring, after the chance for severe cold temperatures has passed, vines are uncovered and pruned back to two to three buds. This channels the vine's energy into two to three growing points and will help trunks grow straight and rapidly to the trellis wire. In

---

FIGURE 4

Areas subject to radiation frost on calm nights.

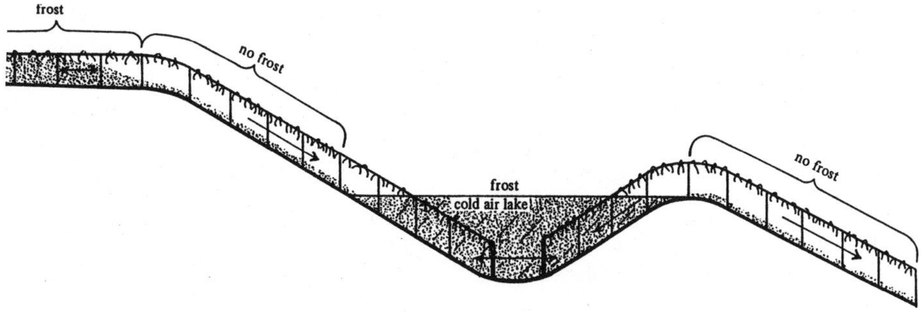

Washington, two trunks are preferred over one. Grow tubes are helpful at this time to enhance growth, help train the vine, and protect young vines. When the vine reaches the support wire or cordon wire of the trellis, the trunks, if there are two of them, are bent in each direction along the wire. If there is only one trunk, then the vine is headed at the wire, and laterals growing from buds below the heading cut will be trained along the wire. Since the canes trained along the wire will become the permanent arms or cordons, it is important that all bud locations along the cane remain productive. To ensure this, each cane is pruned back to five to six buds when vines go dormant. This leaves 10 to 12 buds per vine (six on each cane, trained in opposite directions on the wire).

Vines are allowed to crop in the third year. The cordons are extended to fill the space between vines by bending down shoots growing from terminal buds on the fruiting canes. Sucker growth is removed from vines as it appears. In years of winter injury, it is important not to remove suckers prematurely, as they may be needed to renew trunks.

The best time to prune vines is in early spring. The later the vine is pruned, the better the chance of compensating for winter-injured buds. Delayed pruning also can help control certain diseases.

If there is winter injury, it can be assessed by cutting buds from representative areas of the vineyard. The number of buds injured can then be compensated for by leaving additional buds when pruning (Wolfe, W., 1991).

Bud numbers to leave at the time of pruning are determined by the variety, cluster size, and vigor of the vine. For Concord grapes, a formula for eastern Washington has been established that balances the bud number and subsequent crop with the vigor of the vine. To use the formula, a representative vine must be pruned. The one-year-old wood is collected and weighed. Bud number is determined by the weight of prunings. For the first pound of pruning, leave 50 buds; for each subsequent pound, 10 more buds are left, up to a total of 90 buds. Slightly more buds can be left on expanded trellises like the Geneva Double Curtain. For example, if a representative vine is pruned and the one-year-old wood is weighed and comes to three pounds, 70 buds (50 for the first pound and 10 for each subsequent pound) should remain after pruning.

This formula does not work well for wine grapes. Most growers will leave a prescribed bud number and thin if large crops develop. As a general rule 25 to 40 buds are left for large clustered grapes (Chenin Blanc, Semillon, table grapes); 40 to 50 buds are left for medium-sized clustered grapes (Cabernet Sauvignon, Chardonnay); and 50 to 70 buds are left for small clustered grapes (Gewurztraminer, Sauvignon Blanc).

Under eastern Washington's severe winter conditions, it is expected that there will be periodic winter injury to vines. This could take several forms, but the one that most frequently leads to replacement of trunks or cordons is the midwinter cold snap that drops temperatures below -10°F. Should cordons receive severe enough injury to affect fruiting locations, they should be renewed by cutting them off and retraining a cane along the wire. When trunks must be renewed, it is important to retain suckers. Several suckers should be retained to disperse the vigor of a mature root system supplying a small number of growing points. Under this situation, four to six suckers are trained up onto the wire and only cut off when the vine starts producing fruit again.

MANAGING PESTS AND DISORDERS

Even though eastern Washington has reduced pressure from pests because of its low rainfall and isolated northern location, there are major problems with pests and disorders that can only be controlled by careful observation, immediate response to infestation, and close adherence to quarantine laws and regulations.

Washington has had very few problems with viruses. This can be attributed to the strict certification laws which prohibit importation into the state of noncertified grape material. Phylloxera, a grape insect which has no chemical control, is another pest that is being controlled by the Washington State Department of Agriculture's certification program. There are many other insects or diseases that could potentially become problems in Washington and are being held at bay by the certification program.

In the past, a disorder that has been a serious problem for grapevines, is herbicide drift. Because the Washington grape-growing areas are downwind from large acreages of wheat, there have been incidences of drift, causing leaf discoloration and distortion, reduction of growth, and yield loss. Current spray regulations imposed by the Washington State Department of Agriculture appear to have substantially reduced this problem.

COLD SURVIVAL

Cultural practices used in warmer climates may not be appropriate or may have to be modified for eastern Washington's cool conditions. These practices start with site selection, which might be the most important decision made to avoid cold injury. The selection and placement of varieties can also become critical in years of cold injury. Varieties that are cold hardy and can be harvested before November have the best chance of cropping consistency. High-income, cold-tender varieties should only be planted in the best locations. Less valuable, cold-tolerant varieties should be used for cooler locations. Viruses, crown gall, and other pest problems reduce the vine's ability to survive cold winters and make the selection of certified nursery stock paramount (Wolfe, 1991).

Low rainfall in eastern Washington and the use of irrigation can be an asset in regulating vine vigor and assisting with hardiness. Vines that receive limited irrigation early in the growing season produce higher quality fruit and a more manageable canopy. Water stress late in the growing season can hasten dormancy. A final irrigation after harvest, before the ground freezes, helps insulate roots from severe winter cold. The judicial use of nitrogen fertilizer can similarly help manage vigor and hasten dormancy.

Cover crops are used in most vineyards to help maintain low to moderately vigorous vines. Cover crops grown between the rows can compete with the vines for water and nitrogen, and can help with high vigor problems. At the same time, cover crops provide weed control, soil conditioning, and reduce dust in the vineyard (Wample, 1991).

Regulating crop load is one of the more important practices that assist in maturing the grapes and increasing hardiness in the vines. High yields tend to tax the vines, delay maturity, and reduce the vine's ability to withstand severe winter temperatures should they occur. Expanding the trellis to enhance photosynthesis and the leaf-to-fruit ratio might help increase hardiness in vines slightly, but the expense and effectiveness of this operation needs to be weighed against the difficulty and time required to retrain a winter-injured vine back onto an expanded trellis. Conventional wisdom in eastern Washington is to keep the trellis system simple, making it easy to retrain vines and return to production more rapidly following winter injury (Watson, 1991).

In addition to cultural practices there are protection devices that can be effective. Wind machines are used to circulate warm air, which collects in the inversion layer above the vineyard. These machines are used both in midwinter to increase vineyard temperatures and in the spring and fall to reduce frost injury. Orchard heaters and water are also being used for cold protection.

REFERENCES

Ahmedullah, M. and Watson, J.W. 1985. Site Selection for Crops in Eastern Washington, Washington State University Cooperative Extension Bulletin No. 1358, Pullman, Washington.

Folwell, R.J. 1998. The Economics of Growing Grapes in Eastern Washington (unpublished), Washington State University, Pullman, Washington.

U.S. Department of Commerce. 1975. Fostering the Economic Development of the Wine-Grape Industry, Technical Assistant Grant Project No. 07-6-01508.

Wample, R.L. What Happens During a Freeze: Mechanisms of Cold Injury in Grapevines. 1991 Washington State Grape Society Proceedings, Yakima, Washington.

Watson, J.W. Grapevines Need Anti-Freeze, Too—A Cold Protection Checklist for Vines. 1991 Washington State Grape Society Proceedings, Yakima, Washington.

Watson, J.W. and M. Ahmedullah, ed. The Economics of Vineyard Establishment and Management, Pacific Northwest Grape Shortcourse. 1983. Washington State University Cooperative Extension, Pullman, Washington.

Winkler, A.J., J.A. Cook, W.M. Klewer, and L.A. Lider. 1974. General Viticulture, University of California Press, Berkeley, California.

Wolfe, W. Compensation for Injury in Wine Grapes. 1991 Washington State Grape Society Proceedings, Yakima, Washington.

INDUSTRY PANEL DISCUSSION:
Support Industries for Grape Growers

JOHN (JACK) WATSON, Moderator
Washington State University Cooperative Extension
Prosser, Washington

Prospective grape growers have a vast need for information on a wide variety of subjects. Fortunately, there is a large infrastructure of support industries in eastern Washington State that can provide information, expertise, and materials. One of the best ways of obtaining information is from fellow growers. They can provide the practical hands-on information that can only be offered by someone who has gone through the experience of establishing a vineyard. Another person who should be consulted early in the planning stage is a nursery representative.

The various field representatives employed by processors, wineries, and chemical sales companies are a third major source of information. Their job is to assist growers with the necessary information and materials to produce a high quality crop. Private consultants are also available to assist new growers.

This panel, composed of a food scientist, a vineyard manager, a nursery representative, and a processor fieldperson, will discuss the types of information a prospective grape grower might need, and where to find it.

Working with Wineries

SARA E. SPAYD
Food Scientist, Washington State University
Irrigated Agriculture Research and Extension Center
Prosser, Washington

When I receive a call from a grower preparing to plant grapevines for the first time, the first question I ask is, "Where are you going to sell the fruit?"

The reaction that I usually receive is first hesitation, and then, "Well, I plan to sell them to a winery."

I then ask them, "Which one?"

Quite often, the potential grower is a bit stunned. With apologies to the screenwriters and Kevin Costner, many potential new grape growers believe that, "If I plant them (grapevines), they (wineries) will come (beating on the grower's door eager to buy the grapes)." As those reading this who attended the shortcourse know, that is not necessarily true, unless you have a spectacular site or there is a shortage of grapes.

The potential for the best winery-grower relationship exists when contact is made before the vineyard is planted. Wineries often have someone on staff or may recommend a consultant who will assist in evaluating your new vineyard site.

Do not be offended if the representative or consultant thinks that your site is unsuitable for grape production. As before committing to surgery, get at least a second opinion, or maybe a third or fourth, before giving up on your site. Hiring a consultant to assist with site evaluation, planting, and management of a vineyard may save a lot of money, especially if you have little experience with wine grape production.

Potential growers and current growers expanding their acreage most often ask, "What variety should I plant?"

My response to that question is a question, "Where are you going to sell the fruit?" If a grower plants grapes, wineries are under no obligation to buy the grapes just because the grower decided to plant them. You may notice a running theme to this epistle: talk to the wineries or at least to a winery. Match the variety with the site and the interests of the winery to which you are selling the grapes. Remember, you and the winery are trying to anticipate what wines will be in demand five or more years into the future and not necessarily what variety is "hot" today.

Wine grapes are very different from many other commodities. Often, the major goal of a commodity grower is to attain the highest possible yield while meeting minimum acceptable quality standards. These minimum standards are usually easily measured by some type of objective procedure. With wine grapes, maximizing yields is not in the picture.

The winemaker will develop experience working with your site and management practices. She or he will then begin to develop a feel for the yield which produces the best quality fruit. The standards used by the winemaker are both objective and subjective.

Objective criteria that are easily measured determine whether or not your grapes reach the desired balance between sugar, acidity, and pH. Color for red-fruited wine grapes can also be measured objectively to some extent.

However, flavor is very subjective. Winemakers will evaluate the grapes and wines made from them for flavor and aroma characteristics. Sometimes, these evaluations may seem arbitrary to growers, but remember the winemaker is trying to make wines of a particular style and a sensory profile based on his or her preferences.

Grapes can be sold on the spot market or under contract to a winery. If you are an excellent grower and have a good site planted to a highly desirable, commercial variety, you should be able to sell your fruit on the spot market for a good price even in years of surplus. However, if you are a poor grower (e.g., you ignore sound advice from your contracted winery) you will have difficulty selling your crop even to your contracted winery, because it is likely not to meet minimum standards.

There are at least two general types of contracts: tonnage contracts and acreage contracts.

In tonnage contracts, wineries contract to buy a specified quantity of grapes. If you produce less than your contract, you sell less and receive a lower total return. If you produce more, the winery generally buys only the tons for which you are contracted, at the contract price. If the winemaker likes the quality of the fruit, at least some of the excess tonnage might be purchased at or below the contract price. The winery is under no obligation to purchase grapes in excess of the contracted tonnage. If tonnage is excessive and negatively impacts the quality of the grapes, grapes may be rejected entirely or there may be price penalties for substandard fruit. In years of industry-wide surpluses, you should be prepared to have the overproduction remain unsold.

Acreage contracts should work to the advantage of both the winery and the grower, at least in years when there is little or no crop loss due to weather events. In an acreage contract, the grower is paid a set price regardless of yields. However, most acreage contracts are put in place because the winery has very specific yield limitations and production practices that must be carried through. Usually, these contracts are in place for limited tonnages, for production of high risk varieties and/or for greatly restricted production practices imposed by the winery on the grower. In an acreage contract, the winery is assuming some of the risk from the grower.

What kind of restrictions might a grower see in either a tonnage or an acreage contract? Grape yields will probably be restricted in either type of contract. Tonnage limitations will vary between wineries and sites within a given winery's interests. These limitations are based upon experience with site conditions and grower management practices.

Usually, minimum and perhaps even maximum soluble solids concentrations will be set in a contract. Acid and pH levels are less likely to be specified, but may be specified in specific cases or the absolute extremes that are considered acceptable. Presence and amount of diseased grapes will also be restricted.

Growers will probably also be required to present the winery with a record of all pesticide applications to the vineyard. Preharvest intervals may be specified for some pesticides above and beyond the labeled interval, but never less. Wineries are paying for grapes, not M.O.G. (materials other than grapes). Contracts also specify how much per ton will be paid and the timing of those payments. Usually, payments are split into two increments at specified intervals from time of harvest or specific dates. Method of harvest is also specified, particularly if a winery wants grapes hand harvested. Even the size of delivery containers and who provides them will be included in a contract.

Most wineries like to work with their growers. Often wineries will invite growers to a tasting of the wines made from their vineyards. Wines may be blind tasted against wines produced from other vineyards. Both the winemakers and growers learn from such experiences. The grower develops a vested interest in improving the quality of wines through better vineyard management.

Finally, winemakers and growers need to work together to understand each other's goals and needs. Growers must receive sufficient economic incentives to remain in grape production. Winemakers must receive grapes of sufficient quality to make wines at the level of quality desired.

Grape Nursery Service

VERNON BROWN
Washington Certified Nurseryman, Fairacres Nursery
Prosser, Washington

Fairacres Nursery is a Washington State certified grape nursery, producing both certified and noncertified grapevines. Washington State law requires all grape nursery stock for sale in the state to be sold by licensed nurseries which are regulated by the Washington State Department of Agriculture.

In the 1960s, the grape industry in Washington expanded rapidly, causing grape nursery stock to be imported into the state from anywhere it was available. A group of growers, processors, and research professionals became alarmed that this importation of vines could possibly destroy the industry with plant diseases and undesirable pests like phylloxera and nematodes. They formed the Washington State Grape Society as it exists today.

The grape growers and the nurseries worked together to pass legislation, establishing a grape quarantine to stop the importation of contaminated grapevines (refer to Washington State University Extension Bulletin 1203). This grape quarantine has probably saved the industry, allowing for the success we have today.

The quarantine rules require that all imported grape stock (cuttings or plants) be "certified" and come from a "phylloxera-free area." If a grower decides to bring grape material into Washington, it is necessary to contact the Washington State Department of Agriculture Plant Inspection Division (prior to purchasing), for information on how to obtain the proper documentation and inspections.

Good quality grapevines can be obtained from Washington State nurseries. Cuttings to make a plant are obtained during the winter pruning season and are grown the following spring to fall. Because this is a 12-month process, many growers place orders a year in advance of planting. However, plants may be available from inventory.

Washington-certified vines are available from Washington State certified nurseries only, who have established a "mother block" from cuttings taken directly from the regulated foundation block at Washington State University's Irrigated Agriculture Research and Extension Center, Prosser (IAREC).

These mother blocks are inspected twice annually by the United States Department of Agriculture to maintain the vineyard as disease-free and true-to-variety. Certified cuttings from these blocks are grown under strict regulations and are inspected by the Washington State Department of Agriculture during the growing season.

Noncertified vines are available in larger quantities. Plants grown by licensed nurseries are usually of good quality. Our nursery is very careful about the source of our material. The state Department of Agriculture also inspects these noncertified plants during the growing season. During high stock demand years, many plants are grown and sold (illegally) by other than licensed, inspected nurseries. Seek out reputable nurserymen for your plant needs.

The state has established grading standards which consist of the following:

1 year, #1   at least nine inches of new
              growth and good root.
1 year, #2   at least six inches of new
              growth and lesser root.

My nursery sorts a premium plant from the 1 year, #1 grade. Premiums have the required growth "from within the top four inches of the original cutting." We do this as a convenience to our growers for size consistency. In November, we sort, bundle in quantities of 25, label, and store the plants for the winter. Some growers plant in the fall; however, most growers plant from mid-February to early May. Vines are best planted while still dormant, which varies annually due to weather conditions and variety. Plants are shipped boxed or bareroot by United Parcel Service (UPS), truck freight, picked up by growers in pickups with large tarps or canopies, in bins on flatbeds, in U-Haul trailers, and reefer vans. Any method works, as long as the roots are protected from freezing and drying out. The roots must be kept moist at all times.

What's hot and what's not? Currently the demand is for Niagara juice grapes, Cabernet Sauvignon, Merlot, and Shiraz vinifera grapes. The nurseryman is only one source to obtain advice on which variety to plant. Your site and the ability to market the fruit should also be deciding factors. Contact wineries, processors, and consultants for this advice.

On-Farm Perspective

RON BENITZ
Viticulture Specialist, Sagemoor Farms
Pasco, Washington

For someone who is interested in starting a new vineyard, there are several sources of information.

Washington State University Cooperative Extension is a good source for basic information. Especially important is Extension Bulletin 1588, *The Cost of Establishing a New Vineyard*. This will help growers understand cultural practices, labor requirements, equipment, and costs necessary to establish and maintain a vineyard.

The Washington Association of Wine Grape Growers is helpful with educational information, tours, newsletter updates, and marketing assistance.

The Washington Wine Commission is the marketing arm for wine grape growers and has information on the current state of the industry and on marketing Washington wines.

Other sources of information are industry suppliers, including trellis manufacturers, chemical and fertilizer sales companies, irrigation supply companies, and perhaps most important, grape nurseries. Building relationships with these suppliers will help with obtaining information and future supply needs.

The four major activities that a new grower must give first attention to are site selection, variety selection, trellis configuration, and winery relationships.

Site selection is probably the single most important factor that will influence the consistent productivity of a vineyard and the quality of its grapes. Proper soil, slope, microclimate, and water availability are critical in the production of top quality grapes. Senior water rights or alternative water sources become more and more important, as water resources become less available.

The selection of what variety to plant should be based not only on which varieties are currently in demand, but on market trends and future projections. Market information can be obtained from trade periodicals, wineries, and nurseries. Variety decisions should not be made on wines that appeal to the beginning grower but on broad market trends and winery demands.

Trellis systems should remain simple to facilitate retraining winter-injured vines. Consideration should be given to area, site, soil and microclimate, but a vertical trellis seems to be the best and simplest method. This system is adapted to Pacific Northwest conditions, exposing fruit to light and hastening maturity. All new plants should be trellised for mechanical pre-pruning, hedging, leaf stripping, and harvest. Growing tubes are useful to assist in vine training and to accelerate cropping.

Everything that was mentioned earlier has no value unless the grower has a winery that will buy the grapes. Steps should be taken early to build a relationship with the winery or wineries which will receive your grapes. The winery should be consulted on varieties, cultural practices, and grape quality to make sure the product that is expected is achieved.

Vineyard Consultants

MIKE CONCIENNE
Director of Field Operations, National Grape Cooperative
Grandview, Washington

There are numerous field personnel or consultants that can be invaluable to growers and assist them with most decisions involving the vineyard. Consultants are employed by most processors, many wineries, and chemical and ag supply companies. There are also private consultants with which growers can contract.

Most field personnel will have a good knowledge of growing practices and experience with the problems of growing grapes. They keep abreast of current developments in the industry and usually must obtain consultant licenses, especially those who make agricultural chemical recommendations.

The company (winery or processor) consultants provide the vital link between the growers and the processors or wineries. They provide the growers with information, advice, and recommendations to help produce the best crop of grapes possible. They can help with information and instructions on pruning, training, pest management, water and nutrition management, and crop load management. They assist with harvest scheduling and help with contract changes or replacement programs. Processor or winery field personnel also help with an orderly and timely harvest by making crop estimates, scheduling harvest at the highest grape quality possible, and monitoring harvest operations to inform their employers of any grower concerns.

A private consultant is contracted by the grower, usually on a per-acre basis. They in turn will monitor the vineyard and provide recommendations on pest management, nutrition, and viticulture practices. They also can help with site selection, vineyard establishment, and vineyard growing systems.

Chemical consultants represent agricultural chemical sales companies. They do not charge for their services and rely on chemical sales to the growers in exchange for their advice. Most chemical consultants will scout vineyards for pests and make recommendations for their control. Other services may include sprayer calibration, new product updates, and assistance regarding regulatory requirements.

All consultants can provide advice, recommendations, and information, but it is up to the grower to approve or use them. Consultants can be invaluable, especially for the new grower who should be using them and other informational resources to improve his or her knowledge of vineyard practices.

Site Selection in Eastern Washington: Optimizing Site and Variety Choices

Viticulturist, The Hogue Cellars and Thurston Wolfe Winery
Prosser, Washington

There are two primary concerns in selecting a site for wine grape production: optimizing yield and quality. Optimum yield is important due to its direct impact on the long-term economic success of the vineyard and its indirect impact on quality and crop value. In eastern Washington, the primary factor influencing yield is dormant season climatic conditions—specifically, winter injury from subzero temperatures.

Optimum quality is necessary to assure the long-term desirability of the fruit, both for assured sales and price options. The primary factor influencing fruit quality is the growing season climatic conditions—specifically, the correct heat unit profiles to achieve appropriate ripeness for any given variety.

Successfully achieving these concerns is ultimately determined by the specific climatic profile of a site and the ability to match varieties to this profile.

CLIMATIC FACTORS

The primary climatic concern during the growing season and with the greatest impact on quality is the heat unit profile. Heat units are a measure of total heat experienced by the vine during the growing season at a specific site and have a direct influence on photosynthesis and acid metabolism. For grapes, daily heat units are calculated by subtracting 50 degrees from the average daily temperature as measured in degrees Fahrenheit. The daily heat units are summed over the period between April 1 and October 31. The typical range of total seasonal heat units seen in a premium wine region such as eastern Washington is between 2,000 and 3,500. In general, the more heat units, the greater the ability to ripen grapes, particularly late-maturing varieties such as Cabernet Sauvignon.

Both the rates of daily temperature change, or diurnal fluctuation, and the rate of heat accumulation during the season, or profile, have additional impact on the vine's ability to ripen a crop. Although the heat unit profile of a specific site (microclimate) is important, heat units are largely products of broader geographical zones, such as subregions (meso-climate). Length of growing season, or frost-free period, is another climatic concern to a specific site.

The primary climatic concern during the winter with impact on yields is extreme low temperature episodes. Any midwinter temperature below 0°F can damage wine varieties, with temperatures below -5°F being most critical. Such regionwide episodes occur approximately every five years in eastern Washington.

The ability of varieties to avoid damage from low temperatures is called winter hardiness, and there is a range in hardiness for varieties that is largely genetically determined. However, winter hardiness is a dynamic feature and is affected both by the temperatures immediately preceding the extreme cold and by the rate of temperature change. The process of vine adaptation to these changes is called acclimation. Although this feature of damaging low temperatures is heavily influenced by the general climatic characteristics of the region, it is very much a phenomenon of the local geographical properties specific to each site.

SUBREGIONS

The wine-growing region of eastern Washington is referred to as the Columbia Basin or Valley. Its boundaries are set by mountains to the west, north and east, and the high plateau of central Oregon to the south. These boundaries, coupled with its northern latitude and relative close proximity to the Pacific Ocean, largely determine its climatic characteristics and suitability for premium wine grape growing.

The Columbia Valley can be further divided into seven subregions: Columbia Gorge, Lower Columbia, Tri-Cities, Yakima Valley, Wahluke Slope, Walla Walla Valley and Royal Slope. Each subregion has somewhat unique climatic properties that differentiate it for wine culture.

The westernmost subregion, the Columbia Gorge, is a transition between maritime and continental conditions, sharing climatic conditions of both. It is relatively cool (2,000-plus heat units) and wet, and experiences moderated low-temperature episodes.

To its immediate east, the Lower Columbia subregion extends along both sides of the Columbia River between The Dalles and Wallula Gap with low-moderate heat units (2,300-2,700) and low to high probability of cold damage that is very site-dependent.

The Tri-Cities surrounds the confluence of the Yakima, Snake, and Columbia rivers with moderate heat units (2,700-3,000) and typically low to moderate probability of cold damage.

The Walla Walla Valley is located east of the Lower Columbia with moderate to high heat units (3,000 plus), but with a high probability of cold damage.

The Yakima Valley lies to the west of the Tri-Cities, with low-moderate heat units (2,300-2,700) and moderate probability for cold damage.

The Wahluke Slope is northwest of the Tri-Cities along the Columbia River with high heat units (3,000-3,500) and relatively low probability of cold damage.

The Royal Slope is the northernmost subregion with low heat units (2,000-2,400) and moderate probability of cold damage.

SITE CHARACTERISTICS

What are we looking for in a specific site that makes it desirable for growing wine grapes? The first is choosing from one of the above subregions to provide the desired heat unit profile to fully ripen the varieties of interest. The second is choosing a subregion that is least likely to cause winter damage or that can be tolerated by the hardiness levels of the selected varieties. These two choices may be in conflict depending on the variety and subregion.

Specific site characteristics can further optimize these choices or at least make them mutually compatible. These include slope, terrain (unimpeded air drainage), elevation, aspect and soil type, depth and fertility. Slope, terrain, and elevation all allow for the movement of cold air away from the vineyard site, thus moderating low temperatures and reducing

TABLE I

Relative cold hardiness.

Low	Moderate	High
Chenin Blanc	Sauvignon Blanc	Riesling
Merlot	Lemberger	Chardonnay
Sangiovese	Cabernet Sauvignon	Gewurztraminer
Semillon	Cabernet Franc	Pinot Noir
Syrah		Pinot Gris
Viognier		Pinot Blanc

the likelihood of winter damage and spring frost. Slope greater than 5% is preferred, and suggested elevation is between 600 and 1,200 feet. When the best choice is made, the need for spring frost control is eliminated, and the probability of winter damage is greatly reduced.

Slope, elevation, and aspect also contribute beneficially to the heat unit profile, though in a complex and not always predictable way. Much has been said about the desirability of south-facing aspects in northern latitudes, but they are not critical criteria for site selection.

There are many examples of successful vineyard sites in eastern Washington with other aspects, including due north, growing many varieties, including Cabernet Sauvignon. The degree of slope is far more critical than aspect. Soil type, depth, and fertility impact vine vigor, which indirectly affects winter hardiness and fruit quality. Generally, well drained soils of moderate depth (four feet) and low to moderate fertility produce moderate vigor vines with optimal fruit quality and winter hardiness. These characteristics all interact with the meso-climate of the subregion to produce the vine microclimate.

SITE EXAMPLES

Examples of some of the more successful sites in eastern Washington include Canoe Ridge Vineyard in the Lower Columbia, Reed Vineyard in the Tri-Cities, Seven-Hills Vineyard in the Walla Walla Valley, Hahn Hill and Pearson Vineyards in the Yakima Valley, and the Wahluke Slope Vineyard on the Wahluke Slope. This is not a comprehensive list, but it illustrates the subregion and site interactions discussed above.

Canoe Ridge Vineyard is about eight miles west of Paterson on a ridge of the same name. Its elevation ranges between 700 and 1,000 feet, its aspect is east and northeast, slopes are between three and 15%, and there are no draws. The soil is a loamy sand between 24 and 48 inches in depth. Cabernet Sauvignon, Merlot, and Chardonnay are successfully grown, and winter damage was minimal following the 1996 freeze.

The Reed Vineyard is north of Pasco. Its elevation is about 700 feet, the aspect is west, the slope is between three and 10%, and there are no draws. The soil is a loamy sand, ranging from 24 inches to several feet. Several varieties, including Cabernet Sauvignon, Merlot, Chardonnay, and Sauvignon Blanc, are grown, but there was damage following the 1996 freeze.

Seven-Hills Vineyard is due west of Milton-Freewater at the south end of the Walla Walla Valley on a bench. Its elevation is about 900 feet, its aspect is to the north, the slope is about three percent, there are no draws, and the soil is a gravelly loam of variable depth. Merlot and Cabernet Sauvignon of very high quality are produced, but there was winter damage in 1996.

Hahn Hill is three miles north of Grandview. Its elevation is about 800 feet, its aspect is south, slope is between two and 10%, there are no draws, and the soil is predominantly a loam between two and five feet in depth. Riesling, Cabernet Sauvignon, Merlot, and Semillon are produced. There was variety-specific damage following the 1996 freeze.

The Pearson Vineyard is west of Sunnyside on Snipes Mountain. Its elevation is about 800 feet, the aspect is north, the slope is

TABLE 2

Heat unit requirements.

Low	Moderate	High
Riesling	Chardonnay	Cabernet Sauvignon
Gewurtztraminer	Lemberger	Cabernet Franc
Pinot Noir	Syrah	Sauvignon Blanc
Pinot Gris	Merlot	Semillon
Pinot Blanc		Chenin Blanc
		Sangiovese

between four and 15%, and the soil is a sandy loam of variable depth. Riesling, Chardonnay, and Gewurztraminer are produced. There was minor damage in 1996.

The Wahluke Slope Vineyard is 13 miles east of Mattawa. Its elevation is at 1,100 feet, the aspect is south, the slope is three to five percent, there are no draws, the soil is a silt loam between two and five feet in depth. High-quality Cabernet Sauvignon, Merlot, Syrah, Chardonnay, and Sauvignon Blanc are grown; there was little winter damage in 1996.

VARIETY CHARACTERISTICS

The choice of optimal subregion and site ultimately relates back to the varieties to be grown. The important wine varieties with the longest history in the Columbia Valley include the reds: Merlot, Cabernet Sauvignon, and Pinot Noir; and the whites: Chardonnay, Chenin Blanc, Gewurztraminer, Sauvignon Blanc, Semillon, and Riesling. Grenache and Muscat Canelli are not well suited to the region, and little acreage remains.

Emerging varieties with promising futures include the reds: Syrah, Cabernet Franc, Lemberger, and Sangiovese; plus the whites: Pinot Gris, and possibly Viognier and Pinot Blanc. Growers are experimenting with many other varieties; time will tell if they have a future.

Before discussing their characteristics, it must be noted that the choice of varieties for planting is strongly influenced by market demand and price. This fact, though important, is frequently at odds with climatic limitations, and, in the end, it may be to the economic detriment of the enterprise. Another issue relevant to any new wine-growing region is a relative lack of knowledge regarding the optimal pairing of site and variety. This means that planting decisions during the early development of the region are based somewhat on trial and error. Mistakes in variety-site matching will be made until more experience is gained.

Table 1 lists the relative cold hardiness of the major and emerging varieties. It should be noted that these hardiness ratings are approximate, and, depending on the exact circumstances of the site, cultural practices, and cold episode, they may change. It is common for individual varieties to move from one rating to the next. The ratings for emerging varieties are guestimates based on limited knowledge or inferences from related varieties.

The heat unit requirements, or climatic conditions under which optimal quality can be expected, are listed in Table 2. Again, this rating is relative and is strongly influenced by specific site characteristics and cultural practices. There is flexibility in this rating in that many varieties are successfully grown in the adjacent categories, and, sometimes, any category (e.g., Chardonnay). The somewhat subjective factor of winemaker or "house" style also can influence individual ratings.

MATCHING SITE AND VARIETY

It is interesting to note that many of the high-heat varieties are vigorous and prone to vegetal fruit characteristics when grown in low-heat environments. When comparing the varieties for both cold hardiness and heat units, one can see that the more hardy varieties tend to be best suited for cooler climates and vice versa. This is related back to the environments in Europe from which they originated. This also means that certain cool-season varieties are potentially more forgiving of less optimal sites with lower heat units and colder winter temperatures. Such sites can readily be found in parts of the Lower Columbia, Yakima Valley, and Royal Slope. However, one should seriously question the rationale of planting under suboptimal conditions, and look for sites in the subregions with more favorable microclimates.

Conversely, the least hardy, most vigorous, and highest heat-requiring varieties should never be planted at anything less than an optimal site that maximizes heat units, has moderate winter temperatures, and has the most desirable soil characteristics. Untested varieties originating from southern Europe should be included in this category until more experience is gained. Although one or more of the warmer subregions may ultimately be preferred for the sensitive varieties, examples of desirable sites can be found in most of the subregions if careful attention is paid to the site characteristics.

Vineyard Model

JERRY DECOTO
Director of Vineyard Operation
Stimson Lane Vineyards and Estates
Paterson, Washington

A well-planned and correctly established vineyard can be productive for 20 to 40 years. To take shortcuts in the planning and establishing process will usually limit the life of the vineyard or result in expensive corrections in the future. Selection of the site, varieties, trellis systems, and establishment and cultural practices are key in obtaining consistent production of the quality grapes that are in high demand by wineries.

SITE LOCATION

Assuming that once in production, the grower has secured a market for his or her grapes, the most important decision to be made in planting the vineyard is where it will be located. Because of the potential for cold injury to grapes grown in eastern Washington, only the most favorable sites should be considered. Not only should the site have the required amount of heat units and be protected from cold temperatures, it should also be suitable for the varieties to be planted.

While these areas have been fairly well designated in other grape-growing regions, in eastern Washington, we are just beginning to match varieties with sites. Since there has not been much published on this subject, a new grower must rely on the experience and judgment of other growers, consultants, and winery personnel to assist with this decision.

The most limiting factor of growing grapes in eastern Washington is cold temperatures. Spring and fall frosts limit the growing season and can cause bud and wood damage. Severe winter cold can damage or even kill vines. Any site selection should be made with the intention of avoiding cold injury. This means that sites characterized by south slopes, low elevations, light soil, wind, and close proximity to a large body of water, are most suited to avoiding cold injury to vines. Wind machines and orchard heaters can also be used to avoid cold injury.

The low rainfall in eastern Washington requires that vineyards have a water supply for irrigation. Many good sites are located in irrigation districts which supply ample water in most years. Recent drought problems, however, have made senior water rights and valid well permits important under the current irrigation district system. If the site is not in an irrigation district, then well water must be used. Well depth, water quality and quantity should be carefully assessed before committing to vineyard establishment.

Grapes will grow in most soils as long as there is good aeration and water drainage. Soils in eastern Washington tend to be light, well drained, with good fertility. Soil depth should be at least two feet although shallower soils over gravel or fractured rock are acceptable. Soil pH should be between 6.0 and 8.0. The more uniform the soil, the easier it is to farm. Soils with caliche or hard pan must be ripped. Avoid contaminated soil from landfills, old orchards, or construction areas. Micronutrients may be deficient in the higher pH soil and boron, iron, and zinc amendments may have to be used.

A two to ten percent slope is favorable because cold air will drain off it. Slopes up to 20% can be farmed, but erosion problems make this difficult. A southern exposure is best, but northern exposures can also be used. Avoid low spots with poor air drainage. If they must be used, be prepared to install a wind machine or heaters.

Finally, be aware of the site's proximity to good roads, wineries, supplies, and labor. Check zoning codes to ascertain farming limitations or urban encroachment.

PREPLANT

Although variety selection should be guided by winery demands, there are decisions that need to be made in selecting nursery stock. Young vines should be obtained from reputable nurseries and certified by the Washington State Department of Agriculture to be free of insects, diseases, viruses, and true to variety. One-year-old rooted cuttings should be used. Grafted rootstock is untried in eastern Washington and generally not needed. Unrooted cuttings are not generally recommended because of inconsistent and nonuniform stands that result from these plantings.

The first step in ground preparation is to level the ground, if needed. Low spots must be filled in. If a large amount of leveling must be done, the top soil should be pulled away, the land leveled and the top soil returned. Hardpan should be broken with a slip plow or by ripping. If only a slight hardpan is present, a chisel can be used. The ground is then disked to break up large clumps of dirt and to incorporate soil amendments such as gypsum, lime, or minor nutrients. Soil tests run prior to ripping will indicate necessary nutrient requirements. All large rocks are then removed if possible. Soil fumigation should follow if the vineyard is to be planted in a site which might have soil pest problems (nematodes, verticillium, etc.).

Row direction should be north-south, if possible; however, steep slopes, wind direction, or the geography of the site may dictate that rows be oriented in other directions. If rows are very steep, terracing or rows following hillside contours may be necessary.

Cover crops should be planted in the fall to hold the soil from blowing, to provide tilth, and to keep the soil open.

The most common spacings for vines are 6 x 8 feet (908 vines/acre), 6 x 9 feet (807 vines/acre), and 7 x 10 feet (622 vines/acre). The important consideration in making this decision is the space needed to move equipment through the vineyard, variety and vigor of vines, soil type and fertilization, and cultural practices that will be used to farm the vineyard. Since many winery contracts limit tonnage, high density planting is not necessary. The goal in establishing a low maintenance vineyard is uniformity. To this end, soil differences, slope, and grape variety should be used to separate blocks.

VINEYARD SYSTEMS ENGINEERING

If wells are to be used as an irrigation source, be sure they are engineered properly. If an existing delivery system is in place, consider not only current needs but also future expansion and design. The distribution system should be designed accordingly, with consideration given to such things as holding ponds, size of manifolds and filters, and pipe diameter.

The most common delivery system is by drip or sprinkler or a combination of the two. If a drip system is to be used, it should be designed to deliver adequate water to the vines uniformly and with reliability. If nutrients or other chemicals are to be injected through the irrigation system, it must be designed for that purpose and allowances made for the injection system.

The second option is to distribute irrigation water through a solid set sprinkler system. Advantages of this system are that it can be used for frost protection and cooling if necessary. It is also easier to establish cover crops and incorporate herbicides with a sprinkler system.

A third option would combine a drip system with solid-set sprinklers to give you the benefits of both. The cost of a dual system has discouraged most growers from using it.

The first step in laying out the vineyard is to survey the total area. If the site has steep slopes that would lead to erosion, then rows may have to be planted on contours rather than north-south. The next step is to establish a base line, usually along the edge of the property, along a road, or along the mainline of the water source.

The vineyard should be laid out to maximize row length, which reduces costs and increases cultural practice efficiency. The planting grid can be laid out using airplane cable with nicopress marks on it corresponding to the chosen vine spacing. The cable is then pulled between survey reference points and stakes placed at all plant locations. Vines are planted at marked locations, or a stake is put in place and vines planted to the stake.

TRELLIS SYSTEMS

The trellis system used to support the vines must last the life of the vineyard (and longer). It not only supports vines—irrigation systems can be mounted on it, it aids in mechanical harvest, and it helps expose vines to sunlight. If there is one aspect of establishing a vineyard where cost should not be spared, it is with the trellis system.

At the same time, in eastern Washington's cool climate, simple trellises are best. Simple or basic trellis systems are the easiest for re-training winter-injured vines, and they lend themselves to mechanization of pruning and harvest.

Both wood and steel stakes are adequate for trellising. If steel stakes are used, be sure they are heavy enough gauge to support the vines. End posts should be wood or steel. Windy outside rows may need extra support. The trellis height and configuration depends on the training method selected, intensity of mechanization, and harvest method.

When installing, be sure to use a drip line to hang irrigation hoses if drip is to be used. Thirteen-gauge wire is sufficient for this, as well as the wind wires. Twelve-gauge wires or heavier should be used to support the cordons. When installing end posts, allow enough room to turn equipment at the ends of the vineyard (minimum of 30 feet).

In windy areas, an important aspect of first-year establishment is a windbreak to protect vines and the trellis system. Cover crops will help prevent erosion and allow equipment to operate in the vineyard when it is wet.

First Year

Plant vines next to stakes or at previously designated marks. Planting can be done by shovel, auger, or water planter. When planted, the vine root should be 14 to 16 inches below the soil surface to prevent winter injury to roots. Be sure vines are "watered in" to remove air pockets.

Grow tubes have been proven to assist early growth and protect young vines from wind, pests, and herbicides. Current thinking is that they should be removed during the winter to assist in vine hardiness. Fertilizer can be side dressed or applied through drip as needed. Vine growth and tissue analysis can be used to indicate nutritional status of the vine.

Because newly planted vines have a very limited root system, they should be watered frequently and not allowed to dry out. Several monitoring instruments are available to measure soil moisture. This service can also be contracted locally.

Weed control is of utmost importance for young vines. Weed competition can delay growth and production as much as two years. Middles should be well mowed or cultivated, depending on whether or not there is a cover crop. Maintain pest control, especially for cutworms, gophers, and mildew.

Vines are usually allowed to grow as a bush the first year without training. This allows the roots to establish and will provide strong, vigorous growth the second year. Replant any weak or dying vines throughout the growing season.

Year Two

After any chance for severely cold temperatures in the spring, vines are cut back to two buds. Dead vines are replaced. As canes begin to grow, they are tied to the stake and wire. One or two canes can be used to establish the trunk(s). It takes five to eight passes through the vineyard throughout the growing season to ensure that vines are uniformly tied with straight trunks. Other cultural practices, as in year one, include irrigation, nutrient management, weed control (both mechanical and by hand), pest and mildew control, replacing missing vines, thinning if the crop is too large, mowing middles, and hand harvest if enough fruit is present.

Growers are warned not to try and get a large crop in the second year! Growing and producing a healthy, vigorous vine is the first priority in the early stages of the vine's life.

Third Year

During the dormant season, two canes are extended to fill space on the cordon wire. Other canes are pruned to one-bud spurs. Vines continue to be trained and tied, with an emphasis on making the vineyard as uniform as possible. Vines are shoot thinned, leaving only the strongest spurs.

Fruit is limited to one fruit cluster per spur. The crop is either hand harvested or harvested by machine, depending on the vigor of the vine.

Year Four

The fourth year is a full production year, and caution should be taken to balance the vigor of the vine with the fruit load.

Estimating of yield can be done by taking the average weight of a cluster, multiplying by the number of clusters per bud, and then multiplying by the number of buds per vine and vines per acre. This will give you a rough idea of the bud count to be left after pruning. One to three bud spurs should be used, eight to twelve spurs per cordon side.

Vines continue to be trained and suckered when needed. Leaf removal just after berry set assists growers in improving quality and reducing pest problems. Leafing increases color and flavor and helps balance acid and pH. It can decrease rot and mildew by allowing better spray penetration into the canopy and by providing better air circulation through the canopy. Leafing also improves bud fruitfulness by exposing the area around newly forming buds to more sunlight, and it can help to harden-off wood in late summer.

CONCLUSIONS

Growing grapes which result in award-winning wines is a combination of science, geography, and hard work. There are some basic tenants that all grape growers should follow to come close to producing consistently high quality grapes;

- Plant the right variety in the right area
- Plant rootings
- Work closely with wineries and winemakers
- Establish the vineyard right the first time
- Mechanize as much as possible
- Do not cut costs on the trellis system
- Do not overcrop the vines
- Remember the winemaker needs quality fruit to make quality wines.

Grapevine Trellising and Training: Factors and Choices

ROBERT L. WAMPLE
Washington State University
Irrigated Agriculture Research and Extension Center
Prosser, Washington

The inherent genetic character of grapevines *(Vitis sp.)* is a climbing growth habit that evolved in the Caucasus in the Middle East for the dominant wine, table, and raisin grape varieties *(Vitis vinifera),* and in eastern North America for the juice grape varieties *(Vitis labrusca).* Grapevines in the wild typically grow in the canopy of other tree and shrub species, often dominating the upper canopy. This growth characteristic maximizes leaf exposure to sunlight. Fruit production is primarily on one-year-old wood, therefore in the upper part of the canopy. Hence, fruit was not easily accessible for human consumption.

As the culture of grapes evolved, they were often planted in open spaces, and the vine growth habit was allowed to spread along the ground. Eventually, in an effort to improve fruit quality and make it easier to harvest the fruit, support systems were developed, and pruning practices were applied to restrict the vines to these supports.

With expansion of grape production into new areas, each with its unique set of climatic and soil conditions that influenced the growth potential of the vines, new support systems were designed to accommodate these differences and optimize fruit yield and quality. Thus, the discussion presented here is an attempt to summarize our current understanding of the underlying factors that lead to the selection of a trellis and training system for the production of grapevines.

Although grapevine trellis systems are used in all aspects of grape production (wine, table, raisin, and juice), this chapter will focus primarily on the considerations associated with wine and juice grapes.

ROLE OF A TRELLIS AND TRAINING SYSTEM

In considering the choice of a trellis system, there are numerous factors to be assessed. Among these are the basics of what a trellis system is supposed to achieve, as well as what the goals are for the vineyard site. A fundamental expectation of the trellis system is to provide supplemental support for the grapevines, especially for younger vines. Although the trunk of older vines develops sufficient strength to be self-supporting, the fruit-producing positions are not self-supporting and therefore require physical support. This is especially true for cane-pruned systems, but is also true of cordon systems.

A trellis system must facilitate both manual and/or mechanical cultural operations. Labor costs put increasing pressure on vineyard managers to use mechanical methods for dormant/summer pruning, leaf removal, and harvest. Choosing a trellis system that is compatible with these activities is economically essential for large vineyard operations.

A common goal of vineyard management is to achieve maximum yield and produce fruit that meets at least minimum standards. Accomplishing these goals, which often appear to conflict, can be made easier by selecting a trellis and training system that accommodates the combined effects of the site and grape cultivar being produced. An underlying component in the accomplishment of both yield and quality is the choice of a trellis system that results in good leaf exposure to ensure optimum photosynthesis, while providing the microenvironment that permits good fruit development.

Trellis and training system selection must facilitate disease and insect control. This may be accomplished by minimizing the conditions in the canopy that invite or promote pests and disease by making the canopy structure more accessible to pesticide applications.

Finally, the trellis and training system must be economically viable for the grower. Considerations include not only the initial cost of the materials and installation, but also the annual management costs associated with the pruning and training methods to be used. In Washington, an important additional consideration must be the time and costs required in re-establishing the vineyard following severe weather conditions.

FUNCTION OF GRAPEVINE COMPONENTS

To appreciate the role of a grapevine trellis and training system, it is important to understand the general function of the parts of a grapevine. The so-called permanent structures (roots, trunk, and cordons or head) develop over many years and serve both physiological and structural functions.

Physiologically, the roots are the primary source for water and nutrient uptake from the soil. They are also a source of plant hormones that help regulate vine responses to varying environmental conditions. Roots provide significant carbohydrate storage (primarily starch) during the dormant phase, much of which is retranslocated to the developing shoot system in the spring. Structurally, the roots are responsible for anchoring the vine to the soil. The depth and distribution of roots in the soil are dependent upon soil depth and physical structure, irrigation practices including both method and frequency of irrigation,

and certainly upon the total amount of water applied. Root distribution may also be affected by whether or not a rootstock is used instead of own-rooted vines.

The trunk serves primarily as a conduit for the movement of water and nutrients from the root system to the cordon, canes, leaves, and fruit, while also serving as the pathway for the transport of products of photosynthesis down from the leaves to the roots. Some carbohydrates are stored in the trunk, although much of these appear to be unavailable for other subsequent use. Structurally, the trunk is the major vertical support of the grapevine other than the trellis system. Therefore, it is important to ensure that the trunk develops as straight as possible. Use of training stakes or rods, maintenance of the cordon wire at the proper tension, and selection of the correct post spacing for the site and anticipated crop load are essential in achieving this goal. Trunks that are not straight or are inadequately supported are more likely to bend under the weight of a developing crop and canopy. Crooked trunks are more likely to be damaged during mechanical operations such as cultivation, pruning, and harvesting.

The cordon or vines with permanent arms, or the "head" on head-trained vines is the site where fruitful buds of one-year-old wood are retained for crop production. The presence of canes or spurs with multiple fruitful buds makes this location within the vine one of high physiological activity. In addition to the obvious production of new canes, leaves, and fruit—all of which have some photosynthetic activity—there are many other processes, such as the production and transport of hormones and secondary metabolites, that contribute to grapevine growth and development.

Maintenance of the head/cordon in a stable position is necessary for the successful positioning of fruit to ensure effective pest and disease control and to produce high fruit quality. Therefore, it is important to make the proper trellis/training method selection to support the head or cordon and facilitate these cultural practices. As with the trunk system, it is important to adequately support the head and cordon to avoid damage caused by mechanical operations, such as dormant and summer pruning and mechanical leaf removal.

Because the leaves are the primary source of photosynthates required for vine growth and fruit production, maximizing leaf exposure to sunlight is very important in the selection of a trellis/training system. However, this must be accomplished while achieving the other objectives mentioned above. Increasing the percentage of leaves exposed to maximum sunlight becomes more important in regions with naturally low light intensity. Vines in regions with short growing seasons also benefit from maximizing leaf exposure to enhance photosynthesis for vine growth and fruit production.

Achieving the necessary structural support for good vine growth, with simplicity and accessibility for mechanical operations, and simultaneously producing the balance between shoot growth, leaf exposure, and fruit exposure, constitutes the challenge in the selection and management of a trellis/training system for your vineyard. Although this seems an overwhelming task, it can be done. Remember, however, each site is different, and the process of choosing a system should begin with a complete site evaluation.

EVALUATION OF SITE POTENTIAL
Climate

Before beginning a discussion of site evaluation, it is helpful to define some terms often used in conjunction with site evaluation. First, a clear differentiation between climate and weather is needed. Weather refers to the day-to-day variation in temperature, wind, rainfall, relative humidity, etc. Climate, on the other hand, refers to the long-term averages or trends for these measures.

To facilitate the discussion of different levels of climatic influence, climatologists have introduced the terms macroclimate, mesoclimate, and microclimate.

Macroclimate refers to the climatic conditions that are typical of the region, and extends over an area of at least several square miles. Information used for describing the macroclimate is derived from one or more weather stations within the area being considered and generally represents averages or estimates for the region.

Mesoclimate refers to the climatic conditions within a specific vineyard site. Reasons for such a designation include the effects of local topographical features such as elevation, slope, aspect, and proximity to large bodies of water on the climate within the vineyard. Numerous examples exist to demonstrate how these features alter the local (meso) climate.

Microclimate is reserved for the area within the canopy and immediately adjacent to its surface. Although the microclimate occupies a major portion of the area within a vineyard, discussions about the conditions within the microclimate are restricted to a relatively small area (1-2 vines). Reasons for this are the variations in microclimate that can exist over short distances within a row, and especially across several rows. These differences may be due to changes in soil conditions, vine health, or cultural practices that result in changes in shoot growth, leaf size, cluster number, etc., per foot of row.

Documenting climatic effects involves the identification of the various components that contribute to our overall perception of what climate is. The most obvious and frequently measured components include temperature, precipitation, wind direction and speed, and relative humidity. Extremes of temperature, both high and low, are recognized for their potential effects on plant growth, development, and productivity. We must also be aware of seasonal temperature patterns, which can be important when considering the need for protective measures. Choice of trellis system in regions with frequent temperature extremes must permit adjustments in canopy positioning or ease of retraining to minimize effects of high or low temperatures.

Of greater concern are those regions where sufficient damage due to extreme temperature (usually low temperature) would require retraining or replanting a significant portion of the vineyard. In such areas, it seems advisable to use a simple trellis system. This would allow easy removal of the damaged vines and rapid re-establishment of the vineyard. Careful site evaluation must consider the number of frost-free days, since the length of the growing season limits the species and cultivars (varieties) that can be grown at the site.

Another way temperature fluctuations and seasonal patterns are reported is "growing degree days" (GDD). Depending upon the crop, a critical or "base" temperature is used in the calculation of GDD for that specific crop.

For grapevines, the base temperature is 50°F (10°C). The assumption is that the vines have limited physiological activity below that temperature. To calculate GDD, the base temperature is subtracted from the average of the daily maximum and minimum temperature: i.e., GDD = [(daily maximum + daily minimum)/2] – base temperature. For example, a day with a maximum temperature of 90°F and minimum temperature of 50°F and using a base temperature of 50°F would result in the accumulation of 20° GDD [(90 + 50)/2 = 70; 70 – 50 = 20]. Typical annual GDD accumulations for the Yakima Valley are between 2,300 and 2,880, with a long-term average of about 2,400 GDD.

The range in GDD indicates the potential seasonal variability that can occur in this region. Furthermore, it should be recognized how relatively small changes in elevation or proximity to large bodies of water can influence GDD accumulation. The influence of relative humidity on daily temperature fluctuations, therefore GDD accumulation, is another important factor. Increasing moisture in the air reduces diurnal temperature changes by "trapping" heat during the day and "holding" it at night.

For example, in the eastern United States or in coastal regions, daily minimum temperatures are only five to ten degrees below the daily maximum. On those days when the maximum temperature is 80°F, the nighttime temperature may be 70°F. Using the 50°F base temperature, 25 GDD are accumulated. Comparing this to the example above can be somewhat confusing and perhaps misleading if the effect of relative humidity is not acknowledged. The concept of GDD is often used to classify different growing areas into zones for comparative purposes.

Winkler (1938, *Wine Review* 6: 14-16) developed the following designations, which are often used for comparing grape-growing regions:

Region 1 = less than 2,500 GDD
Region 2 = 2,501 - 3,000 GDD
Region 3 = 3,001 - 3,500 GDD
Region 4 = 3,501 - 4,000 GDD
Region 5 = more than 4,000 GDD

Regions 1, 4, and 5 are considered by many to be marginal for the production of high quality premium wines.

Day-night temperature differentials may also be an important consideration in the selection of a trellis system. In Washington, the primary concern is the potential for low temperature injury to permanent vine structures such as trunks and cordons. In areas where large fluctuations in daily temperatures occur, the loss of cold hardiness which results from relatively high day temperatures (above 50°F or 10°C), can result in increased risk of phloem and xylem injury when the temperature drops below freezing. The frequency of such occurrences is irrelevant, as one instance can be enough to damage vines. If this injury is sufficient to require re-establishment of these permanent structures, and if such an event occurs frequently (every 5-7 years or less), it may be advisable to select a trellis system that permits easy, cost-effective removal of injured structures and retraining.

Seasonal patterns, as well as cumulative precipitation, play an important role in vine growth, fruitfulness, and fruit quality. For regions with high levels of precipitation, especially during the growing season, it may be advisable to select more elaborate trellis systems to accommodate excessive vegetative growth. In addition, these systems may be necessary to ensure light exposure of the fruit to achieve the desired quality. Such trellis systems may achieve fruit exposure by either "positioning" the canopy or by positioning the canopy to facilitate summer mechanical pruning or leaf removal. In regions with low rainfall during the growing season, less elaborate trellis systems are needed unless high levels of irrigation are used which result in canopies too large for the selected trellis system. In low rainfall regions, which are often associated with high light intensities and high temperatures, it is desirable to select a trellis system that affords some protection from excessive heat and light exposure of the fruit.

While temperature and precipitation are dominant factors of the environment, wind can have a significant impact on vine growth and development. Severe winds can result in immediate vine damage and possible trellis damage. Moderate, but consistent winds, especially those from the same direction, can result in vines with unbalanced canopies. Consequently, fruit on the windward side of these vines is often more exposed to light, while on the leeward side, the consistent, strong, directional wind poses potential problems.

Another effect of wind is an increase in the water use of the vines, but there is little effect of trellis system choice on this. Windbreaks are a common and useful approach to dealing with windy sites. When considering the use of windbreaks, considerable attention should be given to the selection, placement, and maintenance to ensure their long-term effectiveness.

Windbreaks can have negative effects. In areas with low light intensities, windbreaks shade a percentage of the vines in each block. Shading will reduce vine growth and fruit productivity, maturity, and, perhaps, quality. The windbreak may also compete for water and nutrients. Therefore, knowledge of root distribution characteristics, as well as water and nutrient requirements, should be taken into consideration in the selection of plants used for the windbreak.

Other Factors

In addition to the climatic factors mentioned above, there are other site characteristics that can influence grapevine vigor (size, seasonal growth, yield, etc.). Some of these are not easily controlled or manipulated, such as soil depth, inherent chemical and nutrient characteristics, and water-holding capacity.

Factors you may have some opportunity to influence or control are soil restrictive layers,

water content in areas requiring irrigation, and supplemental fertilization. Any combination of these characteristics with those discussed above that results in a significant change in vine growth should be factored into your selection of pruning, training, and trellis systems.

CULTIVAR (VARIETY) SELECTION

Aside from the selection of different grapevine cultivars for economic purposes, considerable attention should be given to understanding the mesoclimatic requirements of different cultivars. Inadequate consideration of the inherent growth potential of each cultivar can lead to future problems and additional costs. It may be possible to overcome some of these requirements through altered management practices such as nutrition management, irrigation, and, to some extent, pruning and training practices.

Rootstocks are used to manage insect (phylloxera), nematode, or soil problems (salinity, high pH, or calcareous soils). Grafted vines differ in growth potential compared to own-rooted vines on the same site. In some cases, use of grafted vines and selected rootstocks with apparent growth-limiting characteristics may be considered. However, in many cases, such rootstock-scion combinations alone do not achieve the desired growth, yield, and quality characteristics originally sought.

The scope of discussion on this subject is far too extensive to be fully presented here, and the reader is encouraged to seek other sources of information regarding the expected vigor of various cultivars and rootstock-scion combinations. Seeking input from local vineyard managers, Cooperative Extension personnel, and researchers should not be overlooked, since this information most likely represents the environmental conditions most similar to your own.

BASIC PRUNING SYSTEMS
USED IN VITICULTURE

Pruning is generally defined as the removal of unwanted parts of a vine. This process may occur during either the growing season (summer pruning) or the winter season (dormant pruning). In both cases, the primary focus is new shoot growth or so-called one-year-old canes from the previous summer's growth. Occasionally, older parts of the vine may be removed to restructure or redirect the vine growth. This may be necessary following significant damage due to disease (Eutypa, crown gall) or low temperature injury. Major pruning to remove structures more than two years old is typically performed during dormant pruning.

Summer pruning may involve either hand procedures or mechanical devices.

Summer hand pruning often focuses on the specific removal of current shoot growth that is occurring along the trunk, cordon, or other permanent structure. These shoots are selected because of their location, where they are seen as causing a crowded condition that is expected to result in poor fruit quality or increased disease potential. Another reason may be the removal of shoots that were purposefully left to create an overcropping condition to help control vine vigor. Once this is achieved, these shoots are removed to reduce the crop load and ensure the desired fruit quality.

Machine pruning during the summer is usually directed at removing excessive shoot growth by cutting the apical portions of the current season's growth. Such hedging devices have assumed a variety of configurations, depending upon the trellis system and the desired location for removal of the new shoot growth. An undesirable consequence of summer hedging is the stimulation of lateral shoot growth along the remaining canes. This problem is greatest when the hedging is performed early in the growing season. In the worst case, lateral growth may occur in the fruit zone and result in excessive shading of the fruit and require additional work to correct this problem.

Summer pruning or hedging may also be performed just prior to harvest to facilitate either machine or hand harvesting. In this case, there is usually very little or no lateral shoot growth. In some cases, this late-summer pruning represents the only pruning that will be applied to the vines and is referred to as "minimal pruning." This practice was developed in Australia and has been successfully applied to wine grape vineyards for over ten years.

Summer pruning or hedging should not be confused with leaf removal. Leaf removal is generally restricted to the fruiting zone and only involves the removal of two to three leaves per shoot. There may be several reasons for leaf removal, including increasing fruit exposure, improving penetration of disease and pest control chemical applications, and reducing the potential for disease and insect infestations.

Dormant pruning may also be accomplished by hand or machine. Hand pruning is generally divided into two types, cane pruning or spur pruning. Each may be associated with several different training systems.

HEAD TRAINED AND CANE PRUNED

Several examples of different combinations of head trained, cane pruned vines and trellis systems are presented in Figures 1-3. They are characterized by a primary trunk structure that may be of variable height, depending on the region and desired growing practices. At the top of the trunk, one or more canes of varying length are left at pruning. The number and length of these canes is dependent upon the presence or absence of a trellis system, and its characteristics if present.

HEAD TRAINED AND SPUR PRUNED

The basic structure of this training-pruning system is the same as that discussed above, with the difference being the length of the one-year-old wood that is left at pruning. Either short (2-3 nodes) or long (4-5 nodes) spurs may be left at pruning, depending on the desired crop load. This pruning system is used infrequently in North America.

CORDON TRAINED AND CANE PRUNED

Cordon training can assume a variety of configurations as dictated by the trellis system. Figure 4 shows one example of a cordon-trained vine with cane pruning where the canes and developing shoots are allowed to develop without any additional support or foliage wires. The canes can be of variable length, depending on the cultivar and desired crop load.

FIGURE I

A representation of a head trained / cane pruned vine using the "arched cane" or Pendelbogen on a trellis with three wires or sets of wires. Often there are only three wires, with the lower two used to train the canes and the upper wire to act as a wind or foliage wire. Looping the canes reduces the apical dominance and improves shoot growth along the length of the canes. Where single wires are used at each height, they are attached to the post and there are no cross-arms. Approximate location of the wires is indicated but may vary depending on the site and/or cultivar.

Head Trained / Cane Pruned
with arched cane (Pendelbogen)

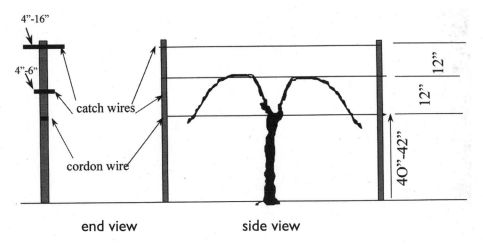

4"-16"

4"-6"

catch wires

cordon wire

end view   side view

12" 12"

12"

40"-42"

FIGURE 2

A representation of a head trained / cane pruned vine using the "looped cane" or Mosel Loop on a trellis with three wires or sets of wires. Often there are only three wires, with the lower two used to train the canes and the upper wire to act as a wind or foliage wire. Looping the canes reduces the apical dominance and improves shoot growth along the length of the canes. Where single wires are used at each height, they are attached to the post and there are no cross-arms. Approximate location of the wires and length of the cross arms is indicated and may vary depending on the site and/or cultivar.

Head Trained / Cane Pruned
with looped cane (Mosel Loop)

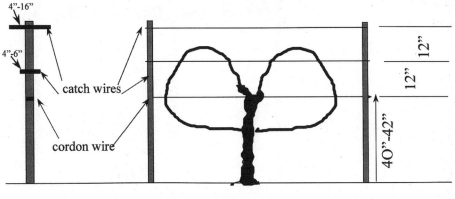

4"-16"

4"-6"

catch wires

cordon wire

end view   side view

12" 12"

12"

40"-42"

FIGURE 3

A head trained / cane pruned vine on a single-wire trellis. The canes are wrapped around the wire and tied in place. Wire height above the ground is variable.

Head Trained / Cane Pruned
no foliage wires

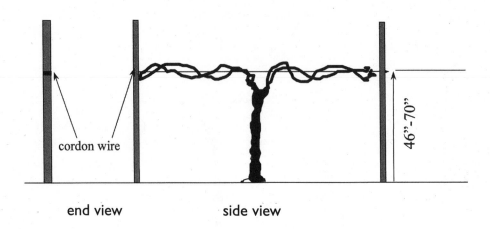

end view   side view

FIGURE 4

A cordon trained / cane pruned vine on a single-wire trellis. A series of short canes are selected, and the remaining shoots are pruned to provide renewal shoots for the following season. Wire height above the ground is variable.

Cordon Trained / Cane Pruned
with no foliage wires

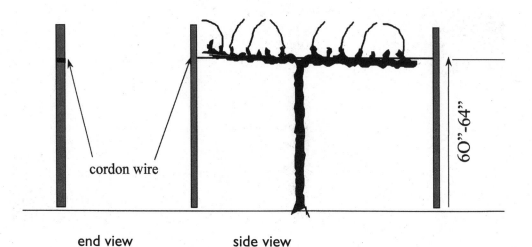

end view   side view

CORDON TRAINED AND SPUR PRUNED

Figures 5-12 present several of the more common cordon trained systems. Perhaps the most commonly used system is the bilateral cordon system that establishes two cordons along a support structure off a single trunk. Modifications of the bilateral cordon system are the unilateral and dual-unilateral cordon systems, where one or two trunks, respectively, are trained up from the ground with each of them being trained along the cordon support.

Another option is the establishment of multiple trunks, each of which is trained out along the cordon support structure. The trellis design and other training practices determine the direction of training along these supports. The height of these cordons above the soil varies with the local environmental conditions and other management practices such as pruning and harvest methods.

As can be seen from these figures, the cordon training system, whether bilateral, dual-unilateral, or multiple trunks and cordons, is perhaps the most versatile, and therefore the most frequently used, pruning and training system.

TRELLISING SYSTEMS

The general growth characteristic of grapevines requires some type of trellis system to support the fruiting structures, while maximizing yield and quality. In achieving these basic goals, several other desirable characteristics, such as good leaf and fruit light exposure, improved pest and disease management, and easier pruning and harvesting methods, are incorporated into the design of the trellis system.

Trellis systems can be divided into at least four groups, using the characteristics described in Table 1 *(page 44)*.

ONE WIRE, UNDIVIDED CANOPY

This is one of the simplest trellis systems and is suitable for head trained and cane pruned, cordon trained and cane pruned, cordon trained and spur pruned, and minimal pruning practices *(see Figures 3 and 4 as examples)*. Its ease of installation and low cost make it desirable, but there are clearly compromises with regard to control of fruit exposure and pest management. A particular problem for vinifera vines, especially in windy

---

FIGURE 5

A bilateral cordon trained / spur pruned vine with foliage wires for vertical shoot positioning. Where single wires are used at each height, they are attached to the post, and there are no cross-arms. Approximate location of the wires and length of the cross-arms is indicated and may vary depending on the site and/or cultivar.

Bilateral Cordon Trained / Spur Pruned
with vertical shoot positioning

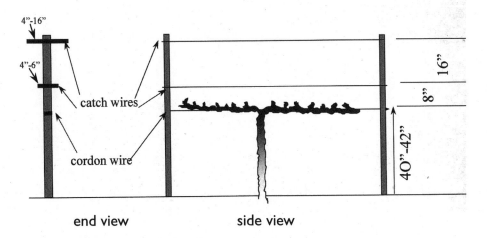

end view   side view

areas, is the tendency for young cordons (1-2 years old) and cane pruned vines to "rollover" once the new shoots begin growing, resulting in excessive fruit exposure and problems with mechanical harvesting. For cordon trained vines, this often requires re-establishing the cordons since they can not be brought back to

the desired upright position the following spring. This problem is a primary reason for the development of the multi-wired systems. Vines that are mechanically or minimally pruned on this trellis system will suffer the same potential problem. However, if the cordons can be maintained in the upright position

TABLE I

Grapevine trellis system classification

Trellis characteristic	Common name/description
One wire, undivided canopy	Hanging cane Cordon trained, minimal pruned
Multiple wire, vertically trained undivided canopy	Bilateral, unilateral, dual-unilateral cordon with one or more wind or catch wires above the cordon wire. Vertical shoot positioned (VSP), Flachenbogen (Guyot Double; Flat cane), Pendelbogen (Arched cane), Mosel Loop (Looped cane)
Vertically divided canopy	Scott-Henry, Smart-Dyson, Ballerina, Sylvoz, Te Kauwhata Two Tier (TK2T)
Horizontally divided canopy	Geneva Double Curtain (GDC), Lyre or "U," "V," Narrow "T" trellis (similar to GDC)
Horizontally and vertically divided canopy	Ruakura Twin Two Tier (RT2T)

These trellis systems are depicted in the figures in this chapter. As much as possible of the details of construction are presented in the diagrams. Additional comments on the use and management of these systems are included here, beginning on page 43. Other sources of information on these trellis systems and their use and management are:

Viticulture Practices (volume 2); Edited by B. G. Coombe and P. R. Dry Published by "Winetitles" at 2 Wilford Ave. Underdale, SA 5032, Australia (1992) ISBN 1 875130 01 2.

Sunlight into Wine: A handbook for winegrape canopy management; R. Smart and Mike Robinson. Published by "Winetitles" at 2 Wilford Ave. Underdale, SA 5032, Australia (1992) ISBN 1 875130 10 1.

FIGURE 6

A unilateral cordon trained / spur pruned vine with foliage wires for vertical shoot positioning. Where single wires are used at each height, they are attached to the post and there are no cross-arms. Approximate location of the wires and length of the cross-arms is indicated and may vary depending on the site and/or cultivar.

Unilateral Cordon Trained / Spur Pruned with vertical shoot positioning

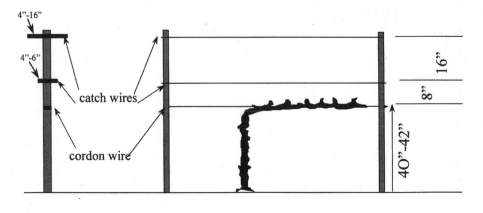

end view   side view

and allowed to develop over the first three to four years, they will have the strength to remain in this position. Mechanically or minimally pruned vines typically have shorter shoots and develop a rather tangled shoot mass that tends to be somewhat self-supporting once established. Such mechanically or minimally pruned vines tend to produce most of their fruit on the outside of the canopy. The continuous addition of shoot mass puts additional strain on the trellis system and therefore requires more line posts and stronger end posts to prevent sagging of the cordons and resulting difficulty with mechanical harvest.

MULTIPLE WIRE, VERTICALLY TRAINED, UNDIVIDED CANOPY

The primary difference between these trellis systems and the single-wire system is the addition of one or more wires that attempt to control the "rollover" problem and spread the canopy vertically. This allows better sun exposure of foliage and fruit, and permits better spray penetration to control insect and disease problems. They are all suitable for the various pruning and training options mentioned above. The variation in the location and number of wires and the choice of pruning and training practice have evolved to meet specific needs associated with the growth and fruiting potential of different cultivars under local environmental conditions.

The simplest of these systems is the two-wire vertical system with a single "foliage" or "wind" wire *(no figure)*. Although this additional wire is intended to prevent the "rollover" problem, it is generally inadequate, especially in windy areas. The success of this system is dependent upon the wind wire being the proper distance above the cordon wire to intercept the young canes as they are blown by the wind or as their weight causes them to fall to one side or the other of the cordon. If all the canes are on one side of the wire, there is a good chance that the cordon will "roll" in that direction, and the catch wire will therefore be ineffective.

The installation of two or more foliage wires above the cordon wire significantly improves the ability to keep the cordon upright *(Figures 1-2 and 5-7)*. These wires may be arranged in a number of ways. If two wires are arranged vertically, the lower one should be close enough to the cordon or developing

---

FIGURE 7

A dual unilateral cordon trained / spur pruned vine with foliage wires for vertical shoot positioning. Where single wires are used at each height, they are attached to the post and there are no cross-arms. Approximate location of the wires and length of the cross-arms is indicated and may vary depending on the site and/or cultivar.

Dual Unilateral Trained / Spur Pruned with vertical shoot positioning

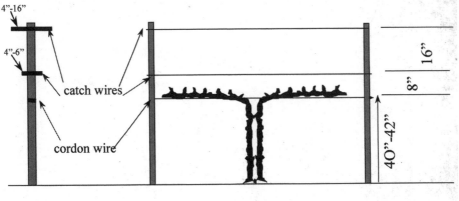

shoots to prevent the rollover problem previously discussed. If the two wires are at the same height, the temptation is to place them too far above the cordon, resulting in the same problem for young vines before the cordon is sufficiently developed to prevent rolling over. If the wires are not high enough, the weight of the shoots as the season progresses becomes too much, and they fall to a horizontal position or, in the worst case, to a downward position.

A possible solution to this is to make the two wires moveable and have two levels above the cordon for attachment. However, this requires additional trips through the vineyard to move the catch wires at the appropriate times. A more common approach to this problem is the addition of three or more foliage wires above the cordon. These still require some additional effort to ensure the canes remain inside of the wires and positioned in a vertical manner.

The distance between the sets of catch wires is variable and is dependent upon row spacing, vigor of the vines, trellis height, machine pruning, and harvesting equipment. The most common arrangements of wires and distances are presented in the accompanying figures.

The use of tightly controlled canopies with two or more sets of catch wires increases the potential for achieving the desired fruit exposure. However, on vigorous sites or with vigorous cultivars, such tightly controlled canopies may require leaf removal because of the small distance between the wires resulting in a crowding effect.

The vertically positioned trellis systems, especially in vigorous sites, require longer posts for the additional wires to direct the shoot growth.

MULTIPLE WIRE, VERTICALLY DIVIDED CANOPY

These trellis systems represent relatively recent approaches to solving the problems associated with excessively vigorous sites and

---

FIGURE 8

A cordon trained / spur pruned vine trained to a Scott-Henry trellis with a vertically divided canopy. The vines are alternately cordon trained to either the upper or lower cordon wires. It is also possible to cane prune with this trellis system. The shoots developing on the lower cordon are trained downward with the lower foliage wire. Shoots from the upper cordon are positioned upward and held between two sets of foliage wires. Each set of wires is typically four to six inches apart.

Cordon Trained / Spur Pruned
Scott-Henry vertically divided canopy

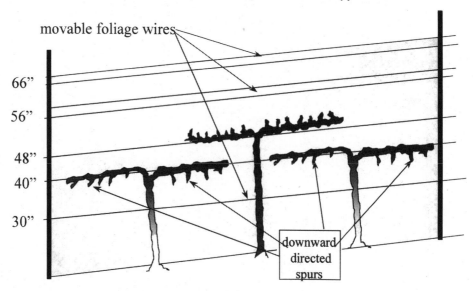

varieties, and sites with low-light intensities and increased disease and pest pressure *(Figures 8 and 9)*.

A significant feature of these systems is that they have the potential of increasing the crop load by the divided canopy. The increased crop load may be used to reduce vegetative growth through competition for photosynthates. The vertical separation of the two fruiting zones also improves fruit exposure and spray penetration for disease and pest control.

Although somewhat controversial, there is some evidence that there is a difference in fruit maturity between those shoots trained up versus those trained down. These trellis systems can result in improved fruit quality compared to standard bilateral cordon systems, particularly in regions with low light, high rainfall, and excessive vine growth. Their additional cost and training expenses may not be justified in regions where vigor can be controlled by other means and where

higher light intensities permit higher crop loads on less complicated trellis systems. Vertically divided trellis systems can be machine harvested and pruned, although the equipment is generally more expensive.

MULTIPLE WIRE, HORIZONTALLY DIVIDED CANOPY

The development of these trellis systems was stimulated by the same basic desires as for the vertically divided systems.

Their advantage over vertically divided systems is that there seems to be no difference in fruit maturity or quality associated with the two sides of the canopy *(Figures 10-12)*. Although the width of the separation between the cordons is variable, these systems generally require wider row spacing than vertical systems.

They are also more difficult to mechanically harvest and prune than vertical systems. However, recent progress in machinery development is overcoming this concern. As with

---

FIGURE 9

A cordon trained / spur pruned vine trained to a Te Kauwhata Two Tier (TK2T) trellis with a vertically divided canopy. The vines are alternately cordon trained to either the upper or lower cordon wires. It is also possible to cane prune with this trellis system. The shoots developing on both cordons are trained upward and held between two sets of foliage wires. Each set of wires is typically four to six inches apart. The height of the shoots from the lower cordons is limited by summer pruning to about six inches below the upper cordon to maintain good light penetration and fruit exposure.

Cordon Trained / Spur Pruned
Te Kauwhata Two Tier (TK2T) vertically divided canopies
(both positioned upwards)

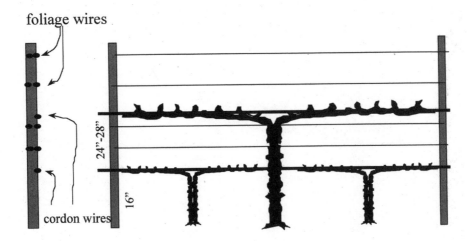

the vertical systems, these also require more wires to accomplish the canopy division. In many cases, the foliage or training wires are moveable to actively position the shoot growth and to achieve the fruit exposure desired.

MULTIPLE WIRE, HORIZONTALLY AND VERTICALLY DIVIDED CANOPY

R. Smart and R. Smith developed this trellising concept in New Zealand in the late 1980s. As with the other divided canopy trellis systems, it was intended to increase foliage exposure under relatively low light conditions, while directing the strong vegetative growth in several ways to improve crop yield and quality. Although successful in their trials, this trellis system has not been adopted in many regions, because of the high trellis and training costs. It also has the disadvantage that it is not easily mechanically pruned or harvested.

In addition to the trellis systems already discussed here, some additional systems include those that are designed on a slant or

angle, or as overhead systems. These are selected most often for table grape production and more recently for "dried on the vine" (DOV) raisin production.

STRUCTURAL ASPECTS OF TRELLISES

The information presented in this section is a brief summary of more detailed presentations found in the two references mentioned above. It should be clearly noted that attempts to minimize costs in the selection of trellis components, without appreciating the role of the individual components, as well as the consequences and costs of trellis failure, is a potentially dangerous exercise in economics. Furthermore, selection of an inappropriate trellis type for your site and cultivar potential can also lead to future expenses in retrofitting the trellis to achieve the necessary yield and quality standards.

With a clear understanding of your site, cultivar, and the anticipated contracted crop load per acre, it should be possible with the help of a qualified individual to select and

---

FIGURE 10

A cordon trained / spur pruned vine trained to a Geneva Double Curtain trellis with a horizontally divided canopy. Cane pruning is also often used with the cordon training with this trellis system. In the system shown here, a single foliage wire is attached to the post 8-12 inches above the cordons. Additional foliage wires can be added to more effectively separate the canopies of the two cordons. In some cases, the foliage wires are used to pull the canes downward to increase fruit exposure. The width of the cross-arm(s) and the number of foliage wires vary with site and cultivar, and other factors such as vine vigor and the type and degree of mechanization used.

Cordon Trained / Spur Pruned
Geneva Double Curtain (GDC)
horizontally divided canopy

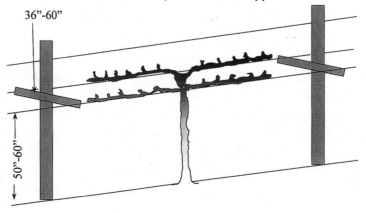

install a suitable and cost-effective trellis system.

There are basically three types of loads and forces on the trellis components—the weight of combined vegetative growth, fruit load, and the wire itself; lateral forces derived from wind against both the trellis and the vines, and lateral forces applied through mechanical devices such as pruners and harvesters; and longitudinal force associated with the tension applied to the wires. Because of biological and environmental factors, these forces and the structures upon which they are applied are not static, but continuously changing.

The primary biological forces are vine growth, which can reduce some forces as the vines grow older and provide structural support, while at the same time exerting more force as the canopy and crop loads increase as the vines reach full production. Other

biological forces might be organisms associated with the decay of wooden posts. Environmental factors include temperature and chemical factors that can change the characteristics of metal posts and wire.

The transfer of the force through the wire to the adjacent posts supports the vine and fruit weight almost entirely. Hence, the distance between posts becomes a critical consideration in trellis design.

With uniformly spaced posts, no missing vines, and little difference in growth or crop load between vines, there is no net longitudinal force applied to these posts. This is because the force on one side of a post is offset by the force applied to the same post from the next set of vines. However, differential crop load, vine vigor, and missing vines can result in a net force to any given post. This usually is not a problem since the force is small.

FIGURE 11

A cordon trained / spur pruned vine trained to a "V" or Lyre trellis with a horizontally divided and vertically shoot positioned canopy. Cane pruning is also often used with the cordon training with this trellis system. In the system shown here, two sets of foliage wires are attached to each post above the cordons. The width between the posts and the height between the foliage wires vary with site and cultivar, and other factors such as vine vigor and the type and degree of mechanization used. This trellis system is not well suited to mechanization.

Cordon Trained / Spur Pruned
"V" or Lyre trellis
with a horizontally divided canopy

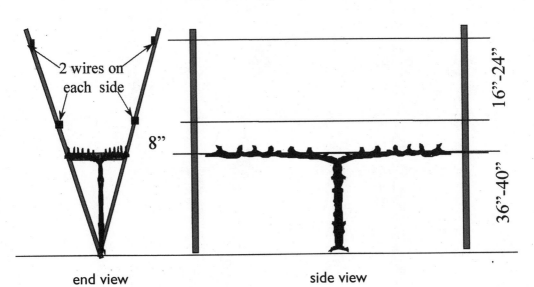

end view   side view

Occasionally, such as during mechanical harvest, this nonuniform force on such posts can result in failure, thus pointing out the need to maintain vineyard uniformity as much as possible.

End post assemblies are responsible for supporting the majority of the longitudinal force of the wire tension *(Figure 13)*.

Wire tension is important to prevent young vines from bending under the weight of the foliage and fruit before the trunk is strong enough to withstand this downward force. Therefore, the end post assemblies must be capable of withstanding the tensions applied to the wire to minimize the sag in the wire between posts.

The farther apart the posts are, the greater the tension must be to avoid bending of young vine trunks. Wire characteristics, such as diameter (gauge) and tensile strength, influence the amount of tension necessary to achieve this goal. Several methods are available for measuring wire tension, and the supplier should be able to recommend the correct value for the post spacing in your trellis system.

End post assemblies become somewhat less of a factor on the total trellis system as the length of the row increases. This is partly due to the structural support of the vines as they age and partly to the fact that as the rows become longer, the effect of a small inward movement of the end posts has less influence on the tension in the wire.

Factors that influence the movement of end posts are: tension in the wire, trellis height, post diameter, depth in the ground, and soil characteristics such as density and moisture content.

The compactness of the soil near the surface is particularly important, as this is a

---

FIGURE 12

A cordon trained / spur pruned vine trained to a "U" trellis with a horizontally divided and vertically shoot positioned canopy. Cane pruning is also often used with the cordon training with this trellis system. In the system shown here, two sets of foliage wires are attached to each post above the cordons. The diagram on the left of the figure shows the foliage wires being moved from the post to the outside of the trellis to horizontally divide the canopy. The width between the posts and the height between the foliage wires vary with site and cultivar, and other factors such as vine vigor and the type and degree of mechanization used. This trellis system is not well suited to mechanization.

Cordon Trained / Spur Pruned
"U" trellis system
(single post or two inclined posts)

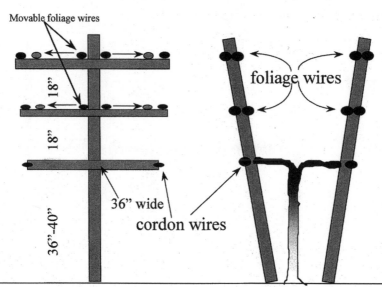

Movable foliage wires

18"

18"

36"–40"

36" wide
cordon wires

foliage wires

major point of resistance to post movement as the tension on the wire increases. Ways to overcome the effects of loose surface soils include increasing post diameter or bearing area in this zone by adding more surface area in the inside portion of the post, or imbedding it in concrete.

Increasing post depth is also important since the stress is related to the square of the post depth. For instance, the stress that an end post can sustain can be more than doubled by increasing the depth from 29 inches to 35 inches. Depending on soil type and depth, careful consideration should be given to the end post assembly.

Various types of anchor systems are available commercially or can be fabricated by most growers. Specific designs should be discussed with the supplier of the trellis materials to ensure success of the system.

CONCLUSION

All of the factors discussed above should be considered both in the process of selecting a site and trellis system. This combination must provide the best structural support for the vines while achieving the desired microenvironmental conditions of leaf and fruit exposure to accomplish the yield and quality goals for your vineyard.

In conclusion, I believe that growers should attempt to keep the trellis system as simple as possible while achieving the desired objectives of balancing vine and site vigor with high quality fruit production. Keeping the system as simple as possible is particularly important in the Pacific Northwest. This is due to the frequency of winter freezes every five to seven years which can require the removal of the permanent vines structures (trunks and cordons) and retraining of suckers onto the trellis system.

FIGURE 13

Representations of various end post assemblies used in grapevine trellis systems. In all cases, the balance of the trellis system is located to the right of the end post assembly pictured.

End Post Assemblies

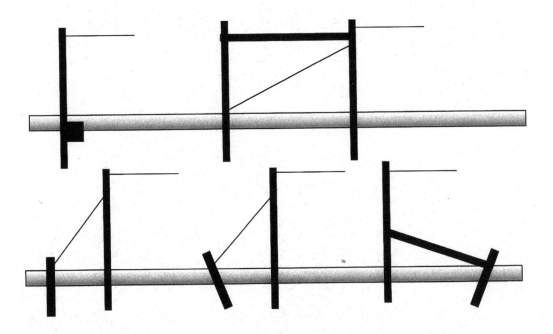

Soil and Nutrient Management for the Vineyard

Robert G. Stevens
Extension Soil Scientist, Washington State University
Irrigated Agriculture Research and Extension Center
Prosser, Washington

S oil and nutrient management are important parameters in managing a productive vineyard. They are, however, only part of the management that is needed, and all vineyard management decisions must be made as a total package that integrates all the needs of the vines. The purpose of this chapter is to give a quick overview of the soil and nutrient management parameters that should be looked at when considering a vineyard site, establishing a vineyard, and maintaining a productive vineyard.

Grapes can be grown successfully under many soil conditions, as demonstrated by the variety of sites producing grapes in the Pacific Northwest. However, soil conditions may play an important role in determining the cost of establishing and maintaining a successful vineyard. The "ideal" soil for a vineyard has been described as being a deep, well-drained soil of medium or medium to light texture with no layers that restrict the movement of water or root growth. We have seen that grapes, especially wine grapes, can, with proper management, be grown in soils that significantly deviate from this "ideal" definition.

As more emphasis is placed on the quality of grapes produced, the uniformity of the vineyard becomes even more important than when just the volume of production is the basis for measuring success. The soil properties and topography will play an important role in how uniform the production and quality is across a vineyard. Factors such as soil texture and depth will play key roles in determining soil moisture levels, thus affecting how the crop matures in different areas. Variation in soil properties must be known and understood to maximize the quality of the end product.

It is important to keep in mind that although it is possible to use poor or infertile soils for grape production, they require significantly more inputs and are much more challenging to manage.

SOIL DEPTH

With proper management, grapes can be grown on soils with a wide range in rooting depth. Concords generally do better in deep, well-drained soils, whereas wine grapes can be grown on shallower soils. Soil depth will play a dominate role in irrigation system design and irrigation management. Soil depth should be mapped during vineyard establishment so the irrigation blocks can be established that allow different irrigation regimes to be used to maintain proper water supply throughout the growing season. When properly managed, it may be easier to regulate soil moisture in shallow soils.

Shallow and moderately deep soils, especially those over caliche layers, may have significant problems with drainage. Poor drainage will lead to periods when the soil in the root zone becomes saturated. During these periods of low oxygen availability, root function is reduced, and, therefore, nutrient uptake is limited. This is especially important with Concords, which can develop iron chlorosis under these conditions.

In the past, with furrow irrigation, leveling was necessary to adequately get water across a field. Now, with the increased utilization of sprinklers and especially drip systems, leveling is not critical to proper water application. On most of our eastern Washington soils, leveling will increase the variability in soil quality across a site and thus increase management difficulties. Therefore, unless absolutely necessary, leveling of new ground is not encouraged.

SOIL TEXTURE

One of the basic properties of the soil that you need to be aware of is the soil's texture. Soil texture is defined as the relative proportions of the various soil separates (sand, silt, clay). The textural name of a soil is determined by the percent distribution of the soil separates. Textural names such as sandy loam, silt loam, or loam can be read from a standard textural diagram after the percent sand, silt, and clay is determined. With practice, the texture of a soil can be determined by the feel in the field.

The texture of both the surface horizon and deeper layers of soil is important because of its influence on water-holding capacity, the rate of water movement through the soil, and nutrient availability. Soil texture plays a key role in determining irrigation method and frequency. The type of pesticide to be used and the rate of application may be affected by the soil texture (see labels).

Variability in crop production across a given field may be closely related to variation in soil texture and related soil depth. A soil survey of the field in question should be obtained from the Natural Resource Conservation Service and verified by in-field sampling. When considering the cost of vineyard establishment and long-term management costs, it is advisable to do a grid sampling on the vineyard site to better map soil texture and depth. This intensive sampling will only need to be done once in the life of the vineyard. Remember, we are trying to develop a database that

will let us manage soils and not just vineyards.

Soil texture will also influence nutrient management. The higher the percent sand, the fewer binding sites there are in the soil to hold plant nutrients. Therefore, sandier soils will generally be less fertile and require regular additions of lacking nutrients.

Remember that rocks do not hold water or nutrients. In soils with a significant content of gravel or rock, this volume must be subtracted when determining water-holding capacity of a given depth of soil.

SALINITY

Vineyard sites should be tested for the presence of salts. Salt damage can be significant especially in the year of planting. When more salts enter the soil than are removed through uptake or drainage, a salt imbalance occurs.

All soils and waters contain some level of salts. Water moving through the soil carries additional salts to low areas. As the water is evaporated or used by plants, deposits of soluble (non-precipitated) salts are left. Restricted drainage is nearly always associated with salinity. Salts accumulate in the soil surface above a high water table because of the capillary rise and evaporation from the soil surface. This occurs where the water table is less than four or five feet deep, but is worse where the water table is shallower than 4 feet. Saline areas also occur where ground water that has moved along caliche or rock layers surfaces at the base of a slope.

Soil salinity is measured as the electrical conductivity of a saturated soil extract and is reported in milli mhos per centimeter (mmho/cm). Soils with greater than 4 mmhos/cm are considered to be saline and will require management to attempt to leach excess salts from the profile. At planting, salinity levels of 1-2 mmhos/cm may cause salt problems for small plants.

Good drainage is necessary to remove salts from the profile. Because of the topography in some areas, drainage is not possible. In these areas, it is best not to try to establish vines because they will be hard to keep alive and if they survive will have very low productivity.

SOIL pH

Grapes can be grown on a wide range of soil pH, as demonstrated by production in western and eastern Washington and Oregon. The soil pH is an expression of the hydrogen ion (H +) activity in the soil. The pH of a given soil is determined by the parent material, climatic conditions, and long-term management practices. In central and eastern Washington, soil pH is normally above 6.5. Areas where free calcium carbonate (caliche) is found, have pH levels in excess of 7.8. Soil pH below 6.5 may be found where high rates of acidifying nitrogen fertilizers have been used on sandy soils.

Soil pH can have a direct effect on root growth. However, more often, the effect of low or high pH is expressed as either a nutrient deficiency or toxicity. High pH (greater than 7.8) leads to reduced availability of nutrients such as phosphorus, zinc, and iron. High pH soils are often associated with iron deficiency (chlorosis) in Concords.

Soil pH can be adjusted. It is important to know if there is something wrong and what you are trying to fix. The addition to the soil of acidifying nitrogen fertilizers such as ammonium sulfate, or acid sources such as N-pHURIC, releases hydrogen ions, thus lowering the soil pH. The addition of elemental sulfur will also produce acidity when the sulfur is microbially oxidized to plant-available sulfate.

On soils that contain free calcium carbonate, it is very difficult to economically lower the soil pH. It is, however, possible to improve nutrient availability on a micro-zone basis. When a zone of acidification occurs around a fertilizer or elemental sulfur granule, nutrients such as phosphorus, zinc, and iron become more available to plants. On high pH soils, rates of at least 500 to a 1,000 pounds per acre of elemental sulfur are recommended at planting. This will improve nutrient availability when the root system is small and developing.

NITROGEN

Nitrogen requirements are quite different between Concords and wine grapes, with Concords generally requiring much higher rates of nitrogen. Soil tests can be used to determine the level of residual nitrate-N in the soil. However, plant growth and plant tissue analysis will generally be better indicators of plant nitrogen status.

The timing and placement of nitrogen applications will also depend upon the type of irrigation system being used, since this will determine rooting patterns and nitrate movement with irrigation water.

Broadcast applications can be used with sprinkler irrigation, whereas rill-irrigated vineyards should have the fertilizer injected four to six inches deep.

With drip irrigation, the nitrogen can be "spoon-fed" to the crop as it is needed. On deep soils with high water-holding capacity that are being drip irrigated, some modification of the water schedule may be needed to get required nitrogen to the crop on a timely basis.

Since nitrogen status of the vines is closely related to grape development and ripening and nitrogen content of the grapes, the end user (processor) of the grapes will need to be part of the decision to determine the amount of nitrogen to be supplied to a specific vineyard. Overapplication can lead to delayed maturity and high nitrogen content in the juice. Excess nitrogen application will slow winter hardening of the vines and increase the risk of winter injury.

Since we are dealing with a perennial crop, it is important to do modifications in nitrogen application rates slowly over time.

TABLE I

Recommended phosphorus fertilization rates for grapes in central Washington.

Bicarbonate soil test level	Apply lbs./acre
ppm	P_2O_5
2	295
4	204
6	159
8	114
10	68
Above 10	0

Slowly increase or decrease the amount of nitrogen added to the crop until the desired growth and nitrogen levels are obtained.

PHOSPHORUS

Generally, grapes have not produced a yield response to phosphorus (P) fertilization in central and eastern Washington. However, cover crops do require phosphorus management and will respond to fertilization. See Table 1 for recommended rates to meet cover crop requirements.

Since phosphorus is very important in the growth of roots, I would recommend an application of phosphorus at planting on soils testing below ten parts per million (ppm), even if a cover crop is not going to be grown. This will help improve the uniformity of root development across the vineyard. This is especially important on sites with areas of calcium carbonate (caliche) in the root zone.

POTASSIUM

Soil test levels can be used to give a general indication of the soil's ability to supply potassium (K) to the plants. Table 2 gives recommendations for potassium additions based on soil test results.

Petiole samples can be used to determine the adequacy of soil potassium for a given growing regime and crop load. In Concords, potassium deficiency has been suggested to be linked to "blackleaf." However, a direct relationship has not been found. As a precaution, potassium levels should be kept at a high level for Concord vineyards that show blackleaf. Petiole sampling and juice potassium levels

should be used to determine needed potassium fertilization in wine grapes.

SULFUR

Sulfur (S) is generally adequate for most irrigated vineyards. Most irrigation water provides some level of sulfur. However, there are exceptions on the Roza Irrigation District, areas above Yakima including the Kittitas Valley, and the Wenatchee Valley. Sulfur content of wells should be checked to determine sulfur additions through irrigation.

When sulfur soil test levels are less than two to ten ppm sulfate, or sulfur deficiencies are suspected through tissue analysis, apply sulfur at a rate of 40 pounds of sulfur per acre. On high pH soils, this can be as elemental sulfur. However, this elemental sulfur will not be plant available until it is microbially oxidized to sulfate.

ZINC

If the zinc (Zn) soil test level is less than 0.8 ppm, 20 to 30 pounds of zinc per acre should be plowed down at vineyard establishment. Additional soil zinc can be added if plants show deficiency symptoms, such as leaf chlorosis (general yellowing). Foliar sprays may also be used to correct deficiencies.

IRON

Iron (Fe) deficiencies are common in Concords but not in wine grapes. This iron deficiency causes light green or yellow foliage (lime-induced chlorosis) and is associated with poor drainage, high water table, high lime soils, high bicarbonates in water, or a combination of these.

Soil applications of iron do not reduce iron chlorosis. Foliar iron sprays or iron in combination with other micronutrients may decrease chlorosis on those leaves receiving the foliar spray.

Proper irrigation management is critical in minimizing iron chlorosis. Some success has been obtained with the use of acid fertilizers placed in the root zone. Iron and zinc can be added with these acid materials. The zone of acidity prolongs the plant availability of both added and soil micronutrients.

TABLE 2

Recommended potassium additions based on soil test results.

Bicarbonate soil test	Apply lbs./acre
ppm	K_2O
60	480
120	360
180	240
240	120
Above 240	0

BORON

Boron (B) deficiency does occur in grapes, especially under dry soil conditions, such as follow dry winters. Where the soil test boron level is less than 0.5 ppm, apply three pounds of boron per acre. Boron should be broadcast uniformly over the entire soil surface. High rates of boron can be harmful, therefore, recommended rates should be followed. Application of boron through drip systems is not recommended.

SUMMARY

Soil and nutrient management is only one part of a successful vineyard management plan. However, it is a critical step that should be given full attention. Understanding your soil resource is crucial to management planning. Investment in sampling prior to vineyard establishment will more than pay for itself over the life of the vineyard. Soil testing should be used with plant and juice analysis to determine nutrient management strategies that will maximize the quality of the end product.

Irrigation management is a key component of nutrient and soil management and should receive emphasis in vineyard design and management planning.

ADDITIONAL BULLETINS FROM WASHINGTON STATE UNIVERSITY

- EB0722 *Symptoms of Grape Disorders in Washington*
- EB0762 *Spray Guide of Grapes in Washington*
- EB0874 *Soil Fertility and Nutrition Management of Washington Vineyards*
- FG0013 *Fertilizer Guide.*

Irrigation Choices for *Vitis Vinifera* Grapes in Washington

ROBERT G. EVANS
Biological Systems Engineering Department, Washington State University
Irrigated Agriculture Research and Extension Center
Prosser, Washington

Wine grapes *(Vitis vinifera)* have been successfully grown in Washington State since the late 1800s. Soil types, topography, and growing-season climate provide a favorable combination for the production of high quality grapes and wine in many parts of the state (Powers et al., 1979). However, in my opinion, the primary reason that we can successfully and consistently grow high quality *V. vinifera* grapes in central Washington, as compared to other "northern" areas like Michigan and New York, is that we can and do control soil moisture. We do not receive enough rain during the summer to satisfy vine water requirements, and the soil water levels become quite low. Thus, the dry, desert climate in central Washington makes irrigation management the largest single controllable factor in vineyard operation that influences both fruit quality and winter hardiness of vines.

The dry climate is illustrated by data from the Washington State University Irrigated Agriculture Research and Extension Center (IAREC) near Prosser, Washington [46°17'49" N latitude, 119°44'07" W longitude, 1,100 ft. (340 m) elevation MSL], where average annual precipitation (1924-1997) is about eight inches (198 mm). Seventy-five percent of the annual precipitation occurs in the seven months from October through April. The average Class A unscreened pan evaporation (April through October) is 49.8 inches (1,266 mm).

This chapter will discuss irrigation needs, the types and advantages/disadvantages of various irrigation systems, suggested irrigation management practices, irrigation system design guidelines, and procedures for successful *V. vinifera* production in central Washington. A short, general discussion of cold temperature protection (frost protection) is included at the end.

WATER REQUIREMENTS OF *V. VINIFERA* IN WASHINGTON

Evans et al. (1990; 1993) reported that seasonal and daily *V. vinifera* water use in south central Washington, based on data on three cultivars from large drainage lysimeters, was about 14.2 inches (360 mm) per year. Weekly water balances for each lysimeter were calculated from the 1985 through 1990 data. Results of the seasonal water balance analyses of the lysimeter data indicate no significant differences in water use between the three cultivars at the six tons per acre yield levels. This directly corresponds to the observed canopy size and general vine vigor, which were all about same. Based on 1987-1990 data, the average annual water use of mature, well-watered vines of three *V. vinifera* cultivars in south central Washington is only about 15.2 inches per year (387 mm), 17 inches per year (431 mm) and 17 inches per year (432 mm) for White Riesling (WR), Chenin Blanc (CB), and Cabernet Sauvignon (CS), respectively (1 inch = 25.4 mm). Daily crop water use is low until mid-June and peaks in early to mid-August, about the same time as veraison.

Estimate of Grape Water Use

Estimation of actual crop water use in this paper is based on ETo[1] (grass reference), and can be calculated by the following simple equation:

$$ETa = K_c \times ETo$$

Where ETa is the actual evapotranspiration (vine water use), K_c is the crop water use coefficient, and ETo is the Penman grass reference evapotranspiration. The K_c values

[1] *Daily estimates of heat units and ETo are available for each of the 58 stations in the Washington State University PAWS statewide weather network to interested users over the Internet on a subscription basis. Real-time climatic data (current within one hour), bulletin boards, several pest and disease control models, frost protection information, and irrigation scheduling using up-to-date PAWS data through the Washington Irrigation Forecaster program can also be accessed through PAWS. For more information, call (509) 786-2226, and ask for PAWS.*

presented in this chapter corresponding to the appropriate date or heat unit summation are multiplied times the daily ETo estimate for each location to obtain the daily maximum water use estimate for wine grapes. The amount of water to apply in an irrigation is the sum of the ETa values since the last irrigation (do not bother with considering rainfall in central Washington in the summer), divided by the decimal irrigation efficiency.

The water use coefficients can be used in any one of several scientific irrigation scheduling programs to keep a running tally on vine water use and irrigation event. Irrigation scheduling will indicate when to irrigate and how much to apply. Contact WSU Cooperative Extension or the USDA Natural Resources Conservation Service for additional information on scientific irrigation scheduling. There are also a number of commercial companies that provide this and other services.

It should be remembered that it may be desirable to maintain a certain level of water stress on wine grapevines during certain portions of or throughout the entire growing

FIGURE I

Crop water use with no cover crop for *V. vinifera* from lysimetric data at IAREC, 1985-1990.

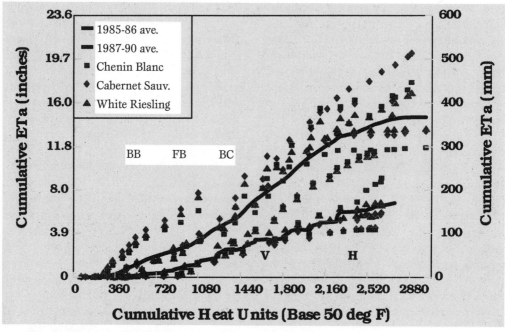

BB - Bud Break   FB - Full Bloom   BC - Bunch Closure   V - Veraison   H - Harvest

season. This will require that the water use coefficients presented here be reduced by some percentage, depending on the grower's objectives.

USE OF HEAT UNITS

Since the wine grape industry is presently used to working in terms of heat units, a 50°F heat unit base (Winkler et al. 1974) has been utilized to present seasonal ETa relationships. This equation is typically calculated as:

$$HU = \sum \frac{T_{max} - T_{min}}{2} - 50$$

Where HU is the daily heat unit summation, T_{max} is the maximum daily temperature, T_{min} is the daily minimum temperature, and 50 is the base temperature in degrees Fahrenheit.

Heat unit accumulations were used in this study to compare the year-to-year water use of grapes in the lysimeters. In addition, temperature data are generally available to growers,

and heat units are easily calculated. Heat unit accumulations generally started April 1, peaked in late July at an average of about 30 heat units per day, and ended on November 1.

WATER USE COEFFICIENTS

The average cumulative crop water use from the lysimeters for White Riesling, Chenin Blanc, and Cabernet Sauvignon grapes are presented in Figure 1 for the 1985-1990 period as a function of cumulative 50°F (50°F = 10°C and degrees are summed in °F) heat units (starting April 1) for comparison. The 1985 and 1986 data (both "one-year-old" vines) were lower because of their small canopy size, and these data lie in a well-defined band below the same vines after they were more mature.

Total field area grass reference evapotranspiration (ETo) crop coefficients for *V. vinifera* grapevines developed from the lysimetric data at IAREC are shown in Figure 2 by day of the year and in Figure 3 by cumulative heat units. These data show that even though bud break

---

FIGURE 2

Grass reference crop water use coefficients for *V. vinifera* in central Washington based on day of the year from 1985-1990, IAREC lysimeter data.

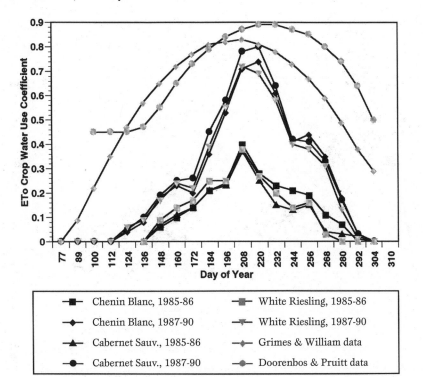

- ■ Chenin Blanc, 1985-86
- ◆ Chenin Blanc, 1987-90
- ▲ Cabernet Sauv., 1985-86
- ● Cabernet Sauv., 1987-90
- ■ White Riesling, 1985-86
- ▼ White Riesling, 1987-90
- ◆ Grimes & William data
- ● Doorenbos & Pruitt data

is typically in mid-April, crop water use rates are relatively low until about mid-June. After that time, water use increases quite rapidly to a relatively sharp peak in mid- to late July to mid-August, followed by a steady decline to the end of the season. This peaking effect closely parallels measured canopy development (data not presented), and may also reflect a slight off-set of the pattern of long daylight hours (and solar radiation) typical of summertime at higher latitudes (both of which have a similar peak). It is believed that these coefficients represent 100% ET values in the vineyard up until about mid- to late August (based on midday stomatal conductance and leaf water potential measurements), after which the imposed soil water deficit for hardening off caused a fairly rapid decline in water use.

The midseason IAREC values are quite close to the midseason Doorenbos and Pruitt (1984) data. It should be noted that if the approximate ET contribution of a grass cover crop (which starts growing much earlier) is factored out of the Kottwitz (1984) coefficients (also developed in central Washington), the estimated net values are only slightly higher than the IAREC values. As can be seen, the

published grape water use coefficients vary widely and are quite different from the IAREC data.

This may be due to several factors, which include: a) variation in the canopy size (water use will vary with canopy, as berry yields are generally controlled by pruning); b) variation in the amount and method of water application; c) different cultivars (or different clones) were evaluated; d) different numbers of frost-free days (if any) that affected canopy development rate and size; e) variation in the accumulation rate as well as the total number of heat units (climate); f) daylight duration lengths across the season; and g) variation in cultural practices (i.e., trellis design and pruning) and soil characteristics.

Based on 1987-1990 data, the average water use of mature vines of three *V. vinifera* cultivars in south central Washington is only about 14 inches (360 mm) per year. Crop water use is low until mid-June and peaks in early to mid-August. These values are considerably lower than published U.S. data, but are similar to average South African (van Zyl and van Huyssteen, 1988) and South Australian (Smart et al. 1974; McCarthy, 1981) values.

FIGURE 3

Grass reference crop water use coefficients for *V. vinifera* in central Washington based on cumulative base 50°F heat units from 1985-1990, IAREC lysimeter data.

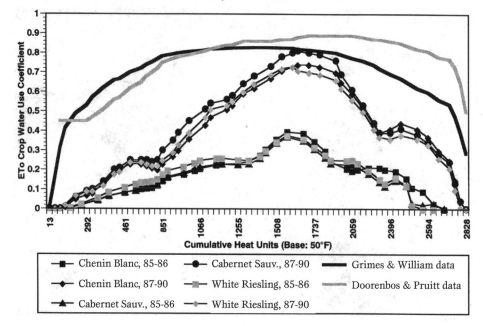

These data are substantially different from those collected for *V. labrusca* in Washington and *V. vinifera* in other areas in the United States. The *V. labrusca* data is dissimilar because of the difference in species. The results from many of these other *V. vinifera* studies appear to be somewhat dependent on vineyard water management (operational criteria of irrigation system/method and amount of water supplied) and soil types, as well as by cultivar, climate, location, trellis style, and numerous other cultural differences. Interpretation and common comparison of these data are extremely difficult.

IRRIGATION SYSTEMS

Advances in irrigation equipment and microprocessor controls make it possible to write a water management prescription for each area of a vineyard. The arid climate of many of the fruit growing regions in the Pacific Northwest allows us the opportunity to very carefully control the amount and timing of water that is available to the plants. If properly done, this can and does have beneficial effects on several critical crop factors, including fruit quality, disease, pests, and winter hardiness. It is also possible to apply various fertilizers and some labeled chemicals through the irrigation systems with great efficacy, lowering the total amount of chemical used, as well as protecting the environment.

Most vineyards are irrigated with pressurized systems except for Concord grapes *(V. labrusca),* where furrow irrigation is more common. Vineyards are typically planted on fairly steep terrain to maximize air drainage during "frost" events. Pressurized systems are better adapted to steep slopes, irregular terrain where land-smoothing is not an option, and coarse sandy soils; all of which are quite common to the major fruit and vine growing areas in the Northwest.

The **design** of a water application system will determine the maximum *potential performance* level for any proposed crop use, whereas **management** dictates the *actual benefits* received and the magnitude of any ecological impacts. High quality installations are more easily maintained and are much less expensive to operate over time than a substandard design

that requires frequent repairs and has a shorter operational life.

Since there is no perfect irrigation system, there is a wide range of equipment available, and each has advantages and disadvantages. The one that a grower chooses to install is influenced by many factors, including personal preference. The major irrigation methods used in Northwest vineyards are furrow, sprinkler, and microirrigation systems. The following discussions present a brief overview of the various methods and important considerations in selecting and managing different systems, but will emphasize microirrigation (drip) systems, since that is the system used on most of the *V. vinifera* plantings in central Washington. In addition, microirrigation techniques offer the most control over soil water.

The first rule of irrigation system design is to keep it as simple as possible. The system must be designed to meet the user's level of expertise and it must fit within their perceived needs and cultural practices. It must be reliable and sustainable, able to manage salts, easy to maintain, and allow for needed tillage and harvest operations.

The design and installation must be site-specific. They are governed by soil type and depth distributions, topography, climate, water quality, water quantity, the proposed crops and cropping systems, as well as the preferences of the irrigator. Designs should facilitate maintenance. Ponds and chemigation installations should be fenced for the safety of workers, children, and animals. Water treatment, filtration, and lateral line flushing must be high priorities.

TABLE I

Irrigation systems.

SPRINKLERS	
Permanent Solid Set	$800-1500/acre
Center Pivot & Linear Move	$400-700/acre
Traveling Big Guns	$500-800/acre
Portable & Wheeling	$300-600/acre
MICROIRRIGATION	
Drip/Trickle	$700-1500/acre
Microsprinklers	$800-1500/acre
FURROW/RILL IRRIGATION	$200-500/acre

Most canal deliveries in central Washington range from six to nine gallons per minute (gpm) per acre, based on peak demands of furrow (rill) irrigation over large areas (e.g., more than 40 acres). Center pivots are often designed to apply six to nine gpm/acre over the total irrigated area. A design application rate of about 12-16 gpm/acre over the total area is recommended for drip and microsprinkle systems that wet a small portion of the root zone in order to meet peak ET_c. Lower rates rely on soil water storage to supplement irrigation applications during peak ET_c periods. (Irrigations will be about 24 hrs./day, 7 days/week at 7.5 to 8 gpm/acre to equal maximum peak demand.) Overcanopy sprinkler irrigation systems will typically require 40 to 80 gpm/acre. System capacity for irrigation should be based on peak evapotranspiration demands in midsummer, usually in the range of 0.30 to 0.35 inches per day.

Surface Irrigation Systems

Because of the need to limit soil moisture for fruit quality considerations and to induce winter hardiness, furrow or "rill" irrigation is not usually an option, except on very deep soils that are normally irrigated only two or three times per year. In these cases, furrow irrigation is only adequate; it does not allow the grower to manipulate soil water content to induce fruit quality changes.

Furrow or rill irrigation typically has the lowest capital requirements, but labor may be quite high. Soil erosion may be a problem on steep slopes, and many growers prefer to have a smooth (no furrows) soil surface to facilitate cultural and harvest operations. Consequently, furrow systems are not the preferred method in *V. vinifera* vineyards. Irrigation efficiencies are often quite low (e.g., 30-40%).

Sprinklers
CENTER PIVOTS

In the late 1970s to the early 1980s, about 2,000 acres of *V. vinifera* were irrigated with center pivot irrigation systems. These systems worked well for irrigation, and their inherent high frequency applications permitted good management of the soil water levels. However,

due to major cultural/pest control issues (i.e., problems with sulfur applications for mildew), primarily related to daily washing of the canopy, all of the center pivots were replaced with drip irrigation systems.

SOLID SET AND PORTABLE SPRINKLERS

Solid set sprinklers for vineyards in the Pacific Northwest are typically over crop. Under canopy systems are usually not practical because of interference by the trellis and canopy. Portable aluminum sprinkle systems are sometimes used, usually in new plantings as temporary systems. Impact sprinkler heads are probably the most common. Sprinkler systems should always be designed such that the pressure differential between any two points in a block is not greater than 20% (10%). Flow variations from individual sprinkler heads should not vary by more than 10% (5%) throughout a block due to pressure. Pressures can be managed by proper pipe sizing, special valving, and/or carefully controlling elevation differences within blocks. Numerous pressure taps/gauges should be placed throughout the entire piping system for maintenance and troubleshooting, particularly on low volume and/or low pressure microsprinkle and misting systems.

Sprinkler heads are usually described by whether it is a rotating or fixed head with three general nozzle types: constant diameter nozzles, constant discharge nozzles or diffuser nozzles. Heads may be rotating or fixed. The rotation mechanism can be impact (spring-driven), gear-driven, or reaction-driven (e.g., spinners, rotators). Fixed heads are fans, jets, or sprayer types.

Each sprinkler type has advantages and disadvantages under different conditions.

TABLE 2

Irrigation efficiencies.

Solid Set Sprinklers	60–80%
Hand-Move Sprinklers	55–65%
Center Pivot	70–80%
Furrow/Rill	40–50%
Microsprinklers	80–85%
Drip/Trickle	85–95%

Selection of a particular sprinkler/ microsprinkler should be dictated by the design requirements for uniformity, spacing, application rates, and costs. Equipment selection is often a matter of personal preference, but a competent designer should be able to accommodate the operational quirks of any particular device into a system that considers physical constraints (e.g., soils, vine spacing, expected vine height, field size, and topography). Constant flow nozzles may reduce flow variations due to pressure changes, but, changing pressures also influence throw diameters and may cause substantial variations in water droplet sizes, affecting their susceptibility to wind, with resulting negative impacts on uniformity.

Microirrigation

Most of eastern Washington's wine grape plantings are trickle irrigated. The high frequency of the irrigation (i.e., daily) and the capability to control the wetted volumes, precisely regulate soil water content, and apply water soluble chemicals gives us the ability to beneficially influence canopy growth, fruit quality, and winter hardiness of vines. These control characteristics are essential for long-term, high quality wine grape production.

Water treatment by filtration and injection of biocides such as chlorine is **always** required with microirrigation systems. This **must** be accompanied by a good flushing and maintenance program!

Drip irrigation, also called trickle irrigation, bubblers, and localized small microsprinklers, microspinners, and microsprayers are collectively referred to as microirrigation. Microirrigation includes any localized irrigation method that slowly and frequently provides water directly to the plant root zone. The slow rate of water application at discrete locations with associated low pressure, and the irrigation of only a portion of the soil volume in the field can result in relatively low-cost water delivery systems, as well as reduction in water diversions compared to other irrigation methods. Drippers and bubblers are designed to apply water at atmospheric pressure, whereas microsprinklers apply water from about 10 to more than 40 psi. Generally, system capacities

from 12 to 16 gpm/acre over the total irrigated area are required.

Microirrigation has the potential for precise, high level management and is an extremely flexible irrigation method to design. It can be adapted to almost any cropping situation and climatic zone. Microirrigation can be used over a wide range of terrain conditions, and it has allowed expansion of irrigated crop production into areas with problem soils (either very low or very high infiltration rates) and poor water quality that could not be farmed with other irrigation methods. It can be installed as either a surface or subsurface water application system.

Microirrigation is characterized by frequent, small, water applications that are placed directly into the crop root zone with minimal evaporation losses. This practice can maintain higher, less variable soil water contents than other irrigation methods, and, normally, only a fraction of the total cropped land area is irrigated. This is both an advantage and a disadvantage for wine grape production. The main advantage is that soil water levels (and plant stress) are more easily managed because the volume of water stored in the soil and available for crop use can be considerably less than the wetted soil volume under surface or sprinkler irrigation systems that irrigate the entire surface area. Disadvantages are that nutrient uptake (especially micronutrients) may be limited, and there is very limited soil water buffering capacity in the event of an irrigation system failure.

The basic philosophy of microirrigation is to replace water in the root zone in small increments as it is used by a plant, at intervals ranging from several times a day to once every two to three days, rather than refilling a much larger soil water reservoir after several days or weeks. Thus, the major concern for scheduling microirrigation systems is primarily how much to apply during an irrigation, since the irrigation interval is often fixed by other factors.

Surface applicators include emitters (drippers), microsprinklers/microsprayers, and bubblers that apply water on or above the surface of the soil. Subsurface drip involves the use of point-source emitters or line source emitter tubing and tapes to apply water below the soil surface at variable depths depending on the soil type and crop. Surface and subsurface drip have also been used for water table control in some humid areas as a variation of subirrigation, primarily on vegetable crops. Microsprinklers may be required to increase the wetted area to maximize soil water availability and avoid leaching on light, highly permeable soils.

Subsurface drip irrigation uses buried lateral pipelines and emitters to apply water directly in the plant root zone. Laterals are placed deep enough to avoid damage by normal tillage operations, but sufficiently shallow so that water is redistributed in the active crop root zone by capillarity. Subsurface drip irrigation requires the highest level of management of all microirrigation systems to avoid expensive and difficult remedial maintenance. A poorly designed subsurface drip irrigation system is much less forgiving than an improperly designed surface drip system. Deficiencies and water distribution problems are difficult and expensive to remedy. These systems require safeguards and special operational procedures to prevent plugging and facilitate maintenance, but they also have numerous advantages.

Due to low pressures and chemigation requirements, hydraulic limitations are tighter than for sprinkle systems. Pressures should not be permitted to vary by more than 10% ± 5% and flows by more than 5% ± 2.5%. Distribution uniformities (DU) should always be greater than 90%. The lengths of run will depend on the specific hydraulic properties of each tubing type, emitter flow requirements, and field slope. In order to maintain high uniformities, lateral lengths of low-flow, low-pressure, thin-walled (e.g., less than 10 mil thickness) tapes should normally not exceed 200 meters. Thin-walled, high-flow tapes are normally less than 150 meters in length. Large-diameter, heavier (greater than 10 mil) hoses and tapes can sometimes be as long as 400 meters or more. Pressure-compensating emitters may be required for small diameter tubing, high operating pressures, long runs, or steep slopes.

Placement of tubing with respect to plants depends on expected cultural operations, emitter spacing, emitter flow rate, size of the root zone, and soil hydraulic characteristics. Typically, row crops have the tubing placed within 0.05 to 0.10 meters of the plant for seed germination and tillage. Placement on permanent crops can vary from 0.1 to 2 meters, although most are within 0.5 meters of the plant row. Tubing can be moved as the plant matures. Tubing can also be suspended above the ground on trellised crops, allowing for easier maintenance, weed control, and less damage by mechanical operations. There should be at least two emitters per vine to ensure adequate water for young plantings and help compensate for plugging or partial plugging of emitters (and it will happen). Generally, individual emitter flow rates of about 0.5 gallons per hour are adequate.

Microirrigation systems normally have some automation because of the requirements for high-frequency water applications. The small pipe and valve sizes also reduce automation costs compared to other pressurized irrigation systems. All proposed control wires, computer interfaces, and data communication links should be carefully considered and included throughout the design process. It is important to remember that the most highly automated system still needs regular human maintenance and management oversight.

A well-designed and well-managed filtration system is critical for every microirrigation installation. It must be supported by appropriate chemical and biological water treatments. Thus, all microirrigation systems should be designed so that biocides, fertilizers and other chemicals can be injected and uniformly applied through the water distribution system. To avoid undesirable leaching, a microirrigation-chemigation system should be designed and maintained to achieve high application uniformities (e.g., DU $\geq$ 90%), since the chemical application uniformity cannot exceed the water application uniformity.

Provisions for flushing pipelines and laterals are required at the distal end of every line in order to facilitate removing fine sediments and other materials that have passed through the filter system. These materials tend to accumulate at the end of the lines throughout the season and must be periodically removed. A common mistake is to undersize piping and valves so that velocities for flushing the main lines, submains, manifolds, and laterals are inadequate. It is important to design for flushing velocities of at least two feet per second (0.6 m/s) at the distal ends of all lines to ensure particulate movement and transport. Colloidal clays or other materials that coat the pipe walls will require higher flushing velocities.

Flush valves and drains should be installed for winter maintenance as well as regular flushing. In areas where damaging freezes can occur, provisions should be made to drain lines above each check valve, solenoid and pressure control valves (and bonnets), and any low points in pipelines. Flush valves should be as large as economically practical.

Microirrigation Emission Devices

Microirrigation methods are generally defined by the water emission device. An emission device ranges from thin-walled plastic tube with simple orifices, microsprinkler, orifice and long path laminar flow emitters and microtubing to more elaborate and efficient turbulent-path and pressure-compensating emitters. Some emission devices are manufactured as an integral part of the plastic tubes and tapes while others are attached during installation.

Two general categories of microirrigation laterals are polyethylene tapes and tubings. Tapes are collapsible, thin-walled, low-pressure polyethylene tubes with built-in emitters or orifices. Tubing is more rigid than tapes with thicker walls and may or may not have pre-installed emitters. Tapes and tubing may also be divided into five classes depending on use: 1) disposable thin-walled surface tape (1 year life); 2) shallow buried tapes (1-5 year life); 3) reusable/retrievable surface tapes (1-3 year life); 4) retrievable surface tubing (multi-year life); and, 5) buried tubing (multi-year life). Tapes are most commonly used on annual or seasonal row crops, while tubing is used more often on perennial crops.

Tapes typically have wall thicknesses ranging from 4 mil (0.1 mm) to 25 mil (0.64 mm), and inside diameters may range from 9.5 to 28.6 mm. Emitters usually have close, uniform spacings (e.g., 0.025-0.60 m) along a lateral line, and emitters are either simple orifices, long path or labyrinth flow paths, or a combination. Emitters may be embossed within the welded seam of the tape or they may be separate, premolded devices installed during fabrication. Currently, emitters on tapes are not pressure-compensating, and water discharge rates of individual tape emitters range from 0.5 L h^{-1} to over 7.6 L h^{-1}. Tape operating pressures range from 7 to about 20 psi.

Tubing has wall thicknesses typically ranging from 10 mil (0.26 mm) to over 35 mil (0.9 mm), with inside diameters from 9.5 to over 35 mm. Preinstalled emitters on tubing have uniform spacing; however, in contrast to tapes, point source emitters and micro-sprinklers can be field-installed at any spacing on the tubing to meet specific irrigation requirements. Emitters are nonpressure compensating or pressure compensating with water discharge rates from 1.5 to over 20 L h^{-1}. Microsprinklers range from about 5 to over 40 L h^{-1}. Operating pressures range from about 10 to over 40 psi.

Emitters can be inserted or molded into the tubing or tape during the manufacturing process. With internal "in-line" emitters, there are no protrusions which interfere with mechanical installation or retrieval of the tubing or tape. Alternatively, emitters (and microsprinklers) can be attached to the outside of the tubing when the system is installed, usually by manually punching a hole and inserting the barbed end of the emitter. This procedure requires more labor, but it allows a system to be customized to match the needs of widely or unevenly-spaced plants.

The labyrinth emitter, designed with long, intricate passageways, will create turbulent flow at normal operating pressures and is often called a turbulent or turbulent-path emitter. The turbulent flow resists plugging by allowing the flow path to be as large as possible and preventing small particles from settling or becoming lodged in the passageway. Flow rates from turbulent-path emitters are also relatively insensitive to temperature fluctuations, thus avoiding a major cause of nonuniform water application under field conditions. Currently, most point-source emitters utilize turbulent-flow paths to control the application of water on tubing and some tapes, and are highly recommended for wine grape irrigation in the Northwest.

Microsprinkler or minisprinkler emission devices are generally simple orifices and include small, low-pressure minisprinklers, foggers, spitters, jets, and sprayers that are installed in the field on tubing. These typically apply water to larger areas than drip emitters, but do not uniformly cover the entire cropped area. They are used to irrigate tree crops, shrubs, widely-spaced plantings, and localized grass areas with extensive root systems, especially on sandy soils where lateral movement of soil water is limited by soil hydraulic properties.

Nozzle sizes range from 0.5 mm to 2 mm, and plugging problems are greatly reduced with nozzle sizes larger than 0.75 mm, combined with adequate filtration and chemical treatment of the water. The state-of-the-art for microsprinklers is advancing rapidly, and improved (e.g., pressure-compensating, self-cleaning) microsprinklers are being developed and tested.

A variation of the microsprayer pulses the water jet in short bursts of up to 60 to 70 cycles per minute, which serves to minimize application rates while maximizing the wetted radius. These can be an advantage on heavy soils with low infiltration rates or soils where poor lateral water movement may be a concern.

Plugging of Microirrigation Systems

Partial or total plugging of emitters is a chronic problem, and the most serious constraint to the long-term operation of any microirrigation system. Inadequate consideration of the physical, biological, and chemical characteristics of the water supply will result in serious plugging problems. The most critical design factors affecting plugging are: 1) emitter design; 2) filtration; and, 3) the chemical water treatment system. System operation and maintenance, including inadequate flushing of pipelines, will also have major effects on microirrigation plugging problems. However, the importance of proper emitter selection to avoid particulate accumulations cannot be overemphasized.

CAUSES OF PLUGGING

Plugging of microirrigation systems may occur from single or multiple factors. Physical factors such as suspended colloidal clays, silts, and other materials passing through filters; broken pipes; root intrusion; and aspiration of soil particles into the emitter orifices are common physical causes of plugging. Chemical factors such as precipitation of carbonates and iron oxides, and precipitates from chemical injections are significant causes of emitter plugging. Likewise, organic and biological factors such as oils, algae, aquatic weeds, insects, fish, frogs, spiders, fungi, and bacteria can be major contributors. Low system pressures and flow rates may also exacerbate plugging problems.

The most common causes of plugging are precipitates of iron, calcium, and magnesium dissolved in irrigation water. Changes in water pH, temperature, pressure, dissolved oxygen, chlorination, and other chemical injections can induce chemical precipitations.

Soil bacteria can sometimes be aspirated back into an emitter and produce slimes that glue small particles together and plug the orifices. Root intrusion is a major problem with subsurface drip irrigation. It can be minimized by chemicals, emitter design, and water management. Chemical controls include the use of slow-release herbicides (e.g., triflurilan) embedded into emitters or injected at low rates (where permitted by the pesticide label), or careful, periodic injections of soil fumigants (e.g., metham sodium) through the water. Other chemical measures include frequent injection of chlorine (e.g., 7-8 ppm) to discourage root growth near emitters. Injection of high quality phosphoric acid at about 15 ppm on a continuous basis will reduce root growth by acidifying the soil and also provides some control for algae but may not affect certain bacteria. Root intrusion control programs often require use of several measures.

Chemigation

Microirrigation offers tremendous benefits for chemical injection and applications. Consistent soil water contents and wetted soil volumes tend to increase plant uptake efficacy of many chemicals. Water-soluble nutrients can be injected to closely match crop requirements, increase nutrient use efficiencies, and reduce costs. Systemic pesticides and some soil fumigants may be injected with high efficacy, if labeled. Injection rates should not exceed 0.1% of the system flow rate. Chlorine and pesticide injections will usually be lower than 0.1%.

All chemical injections should be filtered. Injection should occur after the pump and before the media or final screen filters, to trap any undissolved material. Injection installations should always provide for complete mixing and uniform concentrations before the chemicals reach the field. Materials should be injected into the center of the water flow to ensure quick dilution to reduce deterioration of the filter tanks, piping, valving, or other components.

The use of positive displacement pumps is recommended for liquid chemical injections. The pumps should be adjustable and able to inject any water-soluble chemical at low concentration levels (e.g., 1–100 ppm). The use of an in-line mixing chamber after injection is recommended.

A flow meter or other flow detection device can be connected to a controller that is programmed to inject a specified amount of chemical from a nurse tank into the irrigation system at specific times. Injection rates with orifice or venturi-type injectors are very sensitive to system hydraulic pressure changes and should be carefully monitored and system pressures rigidly controlled.

Fertilizers and other agrichemicals (except chlorine) should never be left in the pipeline when the system is not operating. Pesticide and fertilizer injections should be made in small, frequent doses that fit within scheduled irrigation intervals that match plant water use to avoid unnecessary leaching. All system components must be able to withstand the effects of corrosion from injected basic and acidic chemicals at the expected concentrations at each location.

The general "one-fourth" rule of thumb is that chemigation should start after one-fourth of the irrigation set time; injection should occur during the middle two-fourths; and the lines should be flushed with clean water during the last one-fourth of an irrigation event.

Some micronutrients, such as boron, should be injected with great care, using multiple small applications through a microirrigation system, because a minor mistake or malfunction could result in acute toxicity to the plants. Overapplication of some micronutrients may change solubility limits and cause problems with availability of other micronutrients (e.g., excess iron can induce manganese deficiency).

CHLORINE INJECTION

Chlorine injection is the most common and least expensive method to prevent clogging by biological growth (algae, colonial protozoa, sulfur bacteria, and other mucous organisms). Iron and manganese precipitating bacteria can be controlled by chlorine treatments, aeration, or polyphosphates.

Chlorination may be required for iron and sulfide problems or to eliminate microbial problems. This requires a measured value of least 1.0 ppm of free residual chlorine at the ends of the lines. The free residual is the amount of chlorine that is left after the injected chlorine has reacted with all the sulfides, iron, algae, or bacteria. Sufficient quantities must be injected into the system to meet the required reactions to still leave 1.0 ppm residual chlorine. Constant, automated, chlorination is often recommended. Chlorination is most effective when water pH is less than 6.5.

Chlorine is available in several forms. Gas chlorinators provide a lower cost per unit of chlorine than liquid or solid forms, and are commonly used with larger (e.g., more than 5 ha) microirrigation systems. However, chlorine gas is extremely dangerous, and experienced commercial firms should be used to fill chlorine supply tanks, adjust injectors, and fix leaks. Only the highest quality gas regulators should be used. Local regulations may require fencing, automatic leak detectors with alarms, high quality regulators, and safety equipment, including gas masks. Never locate gas chlorinators in enclosed buildings or near houses and livestock containment areas. These installations should always be located in open areas where any gas leaks can readily dissipate into the atmosphere.

Liquid forms of chlorine are also common. Usually a 10 to 14% solution of sodium hypochlorite (NaOCl) is used, which is a more concentrated form of common household laundry bleach. The material is quite corrosive and is injected into an irrigation system in the same manner as a liquid fertilizer. Self-dissolving sodium hypochlorite pellets are sometimes used in small microirrigation systems. Calcium hypochlorite is commonly available in granular form for treating swimming pools; however, its use can lead to calcium precipitate plugging problems and is rarely used in microirrigation systems.

Free residual chlorine, also referred to as unassociated chlorine, at concentrations of about one ppm for at least 30 minutes, is usually sufficient to kill most bacteria and algae. Chlorine tends to associate with sulfides, iron bacteria, slime bacteria, and other water constituents, so enough must be injected into the system to meet the required reactions and still leave a residual of at least one ppm free chlorine at the distal ends of the lateral lines. Use free residual chlorine (D.P.D.) test kits or special specific ion probes to monitor microirrigation systems.

Copper sulfate, chlorine, and organosulfur compounds are used to control algae and bacterial slimes in ponds or canals. The degree of control will vary with light and water temperature conditions. Some chemicals such as quaternary ammonium are effective when algal growth is slow to moderate, but will fail under rapid growth conditions.

ACIDIFICATION OF IRRIGATION WATER

Water sources in arid areas commonly have high pH values. When ground and surface waters have a pH of 7.5 or higher, the potential for calcium carbonate precipitation is high and may lead to emitter plugging, as well as reduce effec-

tiveness of injected chemicals. The key is prevention by lowering the pH of the water supply.

Acidifying compounds are commonly used to maintain a water pH around 6.5 to keep carbonates in solution, reduce bicarbonate levels, improve chlorine activity, and increase nutrient availability. Acidification may also be required to lower water pH to prevent mineral precipitation from some fertilizers. In addition, various acids are often injected to clean deposits from pipelines and emitters. Sulfuric acid is a commonly used acidifier, but it must be used with proper equipment and precautions.

Calcium carbonate (lime) precipitates can be readily controlled by maintaining the pH of the applied water at about 6.5 (a swimming pool pH tester can be used to monitor) by the careful injection of an acidifying agent (e.g., technical grade sulfuric acid [N-pHuric should not be used in *V. vinifera* blocks for acidification because excess nitrogen will be applied]) or a sulfur burner. The use of "spent acids" from smelting or other industrial applications is not recommended. Water from deep wells in central Washington should always be acidified to lower the pH to about 6.5 at all times.

Acidifying agents must be well mixed and diluted before contacting valves and other system components. Acids should be injected before injection of chlorine, fertilizers, and other chemicals, using separate injection ports and pumps. Bicarbonate levels of 100 ppm or higher in the irrigation water may cause plugging, especially when injecting fertilizers such as calcium nitrate.

Filtration

Good filter systems are the heart of microirrigation. Microirrigation systems require that water be filtered to remove contaminants that might enter the irrigation system and plug emitters. Many types of filters are commercially available, and improper filtration system selection can result in an irrigation system that is difficult to maintain and prone to failure.

A filtration system is designed based on water source and emitter characteristics. These systems should be selected based on the minimum particle size and types of materials to be removed. Proper sizing of filtration systems must consider the total flow and pressure requirements of the irrigation system to uniformly satisfy the mature crop during peak water use times even when the filters are partially plugged. All microirrigation emitters require at least 30 mesh filtration, and most dripper lines should have at least 140 mesh.

Filtration systems are generally composed of combinations of different filtering mechanisms, including settling basins or ponds, prescreens, centrifugal separators, media filters, and disk or screen filters. The selection and placement of specific filtration components should be based on the worst expected water supply conditions and loading rates.

Sustainable operation requires efficient and effective removal of trapped contaminants from every component in a filtration system. Thus, cleaning of filtration systems should be automated whenever possible. Cleaning of filters is usually accomplished by a reverse flow of clean water back through the filter to remove contaminants. This process is also called filter backflushing, or backwashing. The backwash water is returned to the source or to a disposal site.

Automated operation based on pressure differentials across the filter will save water and energy by backflushing only when necessary. Nevertheless, even automated filters should be taken apart, examined, and manually cleaned at least twice a year, or whenever there are filtration problems.

Media filters are used extensively in microirrigation filtration systems. These filters use a bed of some type of porous media, and solid particles are trapped within or on the media as water passes through the media pores. In general, microirrigation media filters should be designed to remove contaminants larger than 180 mesh. Media filtration is highly recommended whenever substantial amounts of organic matter (e.g., algae, diatoms, insect larva, freshwater clams), as well as light minerals such as mica flakes, are present. They are highly recommended with all surface water supplies in Washington but may also be required on some wells.

Minimum flow rates through media filters should be about 17 gpm/ft^2 of top surface area in the tanks to prevent contaminates from reaching the underdrains, whereas the maximum flow rates are about 25 gpm/ft^2. Media filters should be followed by a screen or disk filter for final filtering. This protects the irrigation system in the event of an underdrain failure by catching any media or contaminates that could be washed into the pipe system.

Backwash flow rates must be sufficient to expand the media enough to purge all of the entrapped particulates. This typically requires that small amounts of media be expelled from the tank during cleaning. Generally flow rates of 14 to 18 gpm/ft^2 for #16 and #11 media, respectively, are needed, although the optimum flow rate must be determined by field adjustments. Backwash flow rates that are too low will not adequately clean the media, and preferential flow channels may develop. Backwash water should be examined regularly for excessive loss of media. Tanks should also be visually inspected for media loss by removing observation port covers at least twice a year, or whenever filtration problems occur.

PULSED WATER APPLICATIONS

High-frequency microirrigation techniques have been shown to somewhat increase lateral wetting and reduce water and nutrient stresses, but it is especially advantageous when used with chemigation since leaching can be minimized. The increase in wetted diameter is usually greater for heavy soils (i.e., clays), but the lateral wetting benefits are usually limited on the light, sandy soils common to grape growing areas in eastern Washington. It is usually not possible to maintain a perennial cover crop even with pulsed applications of drip on these soils (cover crops, if needed, should be maintained with microsprinkler systems).

As a general rule for pulsed applications, after the initial fill, the entire system for a block should be designed to fill in five percent or less of the total pulse-on time (e.g., a 15-minute pulse should be up to normal operating pressure in less than 40 seconds; a 2-hour pulse within 6 minutes).

When a high frequency irrigation schedule is applied directly corresponding to the evapotranspiration loss in a given time interval (e.g., hourly), the wetted volume will be nearly constant and leaching will be minimized. However, pulsed or cycled systems generally present numerous design challenges, particularly with respect to pipe sizing and pressure controls.

Emission uniformity problems can occur because of the cumulative effects of widely variable water distributions as the system approaches normal operating pressure at the start of each pulse, and the pipeline drainage to lower elevations after each pulse. Since these systems may operate for short periods (e.g., 10 to 45 minutes) several times each day, water will drain from the highest elevations through the lowest emitters every time the system is turned off, causing severe overirrigation in low areas.

The system must also refill for each pulse, which requires more time to reach proper operation conditions, compounding the net effect of nonuniform applications at the higher elevations due to uneven pressure distributions. Use of mechanical check valves or other water elevation controls are recommended to keep the pipelines full between pulses, thus reducing system drainage problems (Evans, 1994).

IRRIGATION MANAGEMENT

The ability of growers to properly implement irrigation scheduling/water management to manage canopy development, as well as the late-summer water stress periods, is critical to the sustained, long-term production in *V. vinifera* vineyards in central Washington. This is particularly crucial on shallow, marginal soils common to many *V. vinifera* vineyards.

V. vinifera grapes are not physiologically well-adapted for long-term, sustained production in central Washington, primarily because of their inability to adequately prepare for winter on their own if overwatered.

When the vines are watered well, they do not respond to photo period or other climatic signs to start shutting down and "harden off" canes and trunks to make it through our relatively cold winters without damage. Traditionally, in central Washington, *V. vinifera*

vines have been induced to start the hardening off process by the imposition of severe drought stress starting as early as veraison and continuing until after harvest. This is also the time when the berries are maturing and sugar is accumulating, making the proper management of this water stress very critical.

Too little water would cause premature leaf drop which undesirably causes photosynthesis and sugar accumulations to stop. Too much water, on the other hand, results in high crops, but fruit maturation and quality are reduced, and winter hardiness may not be advanced sufficiently. Severe winter damage may result.

V. vinifera grapes have very extensive root systems that will explore huge soil volumes even under drip irrigation. Consequently, they will have relatively large amounts of water available to them in the spring that must be carefully managed. Irrigation scheduling and frequent soil water measurements are essential to the long-term management of a *V. vinifera* vineyard.

Vineyards should be irrigated after the first heavy frost and leaf kill to refill the soil profile prior to winter. This is desirable to increase the heat capacity of the soils and protect roots from cold temperature damage during the winter, as well as desiccation.

Regulated Deficit Irrigation

Regulated deficit irrigation (RDI) is a water management strategy that has been shown to benefit *V. vinifera* production in Washington. The key to successful RDI is rigid control of soil water volumes to control vegetative growth. It is made possible by: a) the practical ability to achieve high frequency irrigation regimes (i.e., with drip irrigation); and b) the capacity to carefully restrict soil water by controlling the application amount and the size of the wetted volume of soil available to the roots. This technique deliberately imposes specific plant water stresses during specific growth stages (usually early in the season) using frequent irrigations, but only replacing 10 to 30% of the plant's daily water use. The wetted soil volume contracts from the sides and bottom of the root zone. At the end of the stress period, as indicated by various physiological markers, water application amounts are increased [e.g., 85 to 100% daily actual potential grape water use (ETa)], but soil water profiles are not refilled, and the wetted soil volume remains constant. Vegetative growth must not be reinitiated by excess soil water conditions.

Regulated deficit irrigation has been found to control vegetative growth, increase fruiting levels, advance fruit maturity, and increase soluble solids. Annual water diversions may be reduced by 20% or more. However, RDI requires that adequate allocations of late-season water be available to "finish the crop" and that the system be designed to apply at least peak crop water use on a daily basis throughout the entire growing season. Automation is highly desirable.

Microirrigation Management

A high level of management is required to operate and maintain a microirrigation system because decisions must be made on a daily or every-other-day basis. Managers require a greater level of training and proficiency than for surface or sprinkler systems. They command higher salaries and are employed year-round because of the need to retain their skills; however, they can generally cover three to four times as much cropped area as an irrigator using more traditional methods, primarily due to automation. The higher level of management also requires adoption of ancillary technologies with their associated costs such as irrigation scheduling, soil water monitoring, and frequent, detailed plant tissue nutrient analysis for fertigation programs.

As a general rule, microirrigation systems are less forgiving of mismanagement or poor design than methods that irrigate a much larger portion of the root zone. These problems range from overirrigation and excessive leaching of chemicals, to severe drought, salinity, or nutrient stresses.

Specific management decisions will depend on crop, site, soil, and environmental conditions. However, microirrigation must be managed as both a water and a nutrient application system. Fertilizers and other water-soluble chemicals such as pesticides (e.g., nematocides, systemic insecticides, herbicides) and soil amendments (e.g., acids, polymers, $CaSO_4$) can be efficiently and effectively applied through these systems. Buried drip irrigation systems are particularly amenable to the application of soil fumigants as well as other chemicals that tend to be fixed by the soil particles (e.g., some pesticides and phosphorus fertilizers).

The questions concerning microirrigation management generally center around when to irrigate, how much to apply, how to accurately evaluate the water status of the plant, and integration of other activities with irrigation needs. These decisions are facilitated by adoption of a sound irrigation scheduling program which may be supported with automation and monitoring instrumentation. Chemical treatment of water, filter cleaning, and routine flushing of pipelines and laterals are also fundamental to good management.

Weed control with microirrigation can be a challenge since both wet and dry soil conditions exist over short distances. Widely different weed species, requiring different herbicides for control, will inhabit small areas, but most weeds will be in the fringe areas between the wet and dry soil zones. Fortunately, herbicides labeled for direct application through emitters tend to work well. However, high soil water conditions can cause rapid leaching or degradation of many herbicides. Weeds are often successfully controlled using plastic mulches or multiple spray applications of glyphosate, depending on the crop.

SOIL WATER MONITORING

Soil water sensors are point or small volume measurements in a field that can be used to monitor soil status and to control irrigations. All soil water monitoring devices should be placed at appropriate depths and locations to ensure that scheduling will be appropriate to optimize yields, minimize water usage and minimize leaching to the ground water. Microirrigated soil water distributions are highly variable, and there are major questions on suitable sensor locations and correct interpretation of the readings. Preferential flow is often a major, but largely unquantifiable, factor in soil water distributions.

Consequently, microirrigation scheduling is often "calibrated" to particular sensor placements, with respect to a water emission point, that are correlated with plant water potential measurements or other independent parameters. Calibration is typically required to optimize both water and nutrient utilization. The number of required sensors can be minimized by choosing representative plants and soil types across a field.

Optimal sensor location will also be influenced by irrigation interval, since a soil water gradient will develop from the emitter to the perimeter of the wetted volume during irrigation. This gradient decreases after irrigation due to water redistribution, and the wetted soil volume approaches a relatively uniform water content. Thus, sensors to control daily or more frequent irrigations are generally located within 10 to 15 centimeters of the emitters but may be located further away for less frequent irrigations. Electronic soil matrix potential sensors are often appropriate for these applications.

Sensors that determine when to irrigate are normally placed in the upper one-fourth to one-half of the root zone within the most active areas of water and nutrient uptake. Sensors located in the lower portion of the root zone can be used to control the amount of water applied and avoid excessive applications.

MAINTENANCE

Implementation of a maintenance program is central to the long-term success of microirrigation. A rigorous and consistent maintenance program includes good record-keeping, a strong chemical water treatment program, and regular flushing to keep pipelines clean.

Each component should be routinely inspected and tested to ensure that they function properly. Consistency in all aspects of the maintenance program is the key to successful microirrigation. Detailed record-keeping of irrigation schedules, chlorination, chemical treatments, chemigation, and maintenance activities is mandatory to document maintenance problems, schedule required maintenance, conduct financial analyses, and plan for future improvements.

Injection equipment should be flushed after each use for safety and to avoid corrosion. Pumps, filters, valves, gauges, injectors, tanks, pipelines, and other hydraulic components must be protected from freezing in winter by removal or draining in cold climates. Electrical panels need to be kept free of moisture and dust. Periodic calibration or replacement of flow meters and pressure gauges will be required.

Mainlines, submains, and laterals should be flushed to remove sediments at least once each month or as needed during the season, depending on water conditions. Mainlines should be flushed first, then submains, manifolds, and, finally, laterals. Systems can be manually or automatically flushed. The whole system should be flushed at seasonal startup, at the end of the season, and whenever repairs are made. Flushed materials should be inspected for signs of chemical precipitations, algal build-ups, or root intrusion.

Routine flushing of pipelines is required to prevent emitter plugging from the gradual accumulation of particles which are too small to be filtered, but which settle out or flocculate at the distal ends of pipelines. Flushing velocities must be high enough (at least 0.6 m/sec.) to transport and discharge heavy particulate matter from the pipelines. Flushing should be more frequent when large amounts of debris are present, while less frequent flushing may be adequate if only small amounts of debris are flushed. Applying surfactants or dispersing agents such as sodium hexametaphosphate through the microirrigation system may reduce some plugging problems by preventing the flocculation of silts and colloidal clays, allowing them to easily pass through the emitters or be flushed from pipelines.

Automated flush valves are sometimes used at the ends of the laterals to help flush fine particulates at the start of every irrigation; however, periodic manual flushing is still required. Use of these valves is not recommended since they tend to leak and waste water, requiring extra maintenance.

Monitoring the frequency of primary filter backwashing and pressure drops can direct attention to developing filtration problems.

All filters should be manually inspected and cleaned on a regular basis, and replaced as needed. Ponds, canals, and settling basins require periodic mechanical or chemical cleaning, and aquatic weed and algae control.

Although much monitoring can be accomplished with flow meters, pressure gauges, and remote communication technologies, frequent visual inspection will still be required to ensure that all system components are functioning properly. Regular field inspections will help find emitters that are plugged, identify improperly working flush valves, locate pipes and tubing damaged by coyotes, rodents, insects, or farm equipment, and identify other problems.

Water distribution uniformity measurements should be made on newly installed microirrigation systems to confirm that the system has been properly designed and installed, as well as to provide a basis for later comparisons. Water distribution uniformity measurements should be made before each crop season and compared to the new system evaluations. If this is too labor intensive or is impractical as may be the case for subsurface systems, then, as a minimum, the irrigator should compare actual system flows and pressures at the inlet and distal ends of the system with the initial evaluations. Additional tests may be required for evaluation and adjustment of maintenance and operational procedures during the growing season, particularly where emitter plugging problems are severe.

In general, criteria for emitter flow variation are: 5% or less, excellent; 5-10%, very good; 10-15%, fair; 15-20%, poor; and greater than 20%, unacceptable. Hydraulic coefficient of variation criteria are: 10% or less, excellent; 10-20%, very good; 20-30%, fair; 30-40%, poor; and greater than 40%, unacceptable.

Decreases in distribution uniformity over time are a cause for concern. Although regular visual inspections will locate emitters that are completely or almost completely plugged, they will not identify small changes in emitter flow rates from partial plugging. Frequent examinations of flow meter records and periodic field measurements of emitter flow rate and pressure variations will help track changes in system performance.

Early identification of problems should facilitate special chemical water treatments to clean partially plugged emitters before the problem becomes more serious. Subsequent comparisons, where partial emitter plugging may be present due to chemical precipitation, algae, or other causes, may be made using the Christiansen uniformity coefficient (UCC) or other statistical measures of uniformity. Emitter damage and wear will also affect flow rates as emitters age.

COLD TEMPERATURE PROTECTION

Frost protection or protecting plants from cold temperatures where they could be damaged must also be a consideration in vineyard planning. The best frost protection technique is good site selection.

Cold protection events in the Pacific Northwest usually occur during "radiation" frost conditions when the sky is clear and there is little wind and strong temperature inversions can develop. These conditions can happen during spring, fall, or winter when it is necessary to keep buds, flowers, small fruitlets, or foliage above the "critical" temperatures at which they can be killed.

It is often necessary to frost protect Northwest *V. vinifera* vineyards in the fall to prevent leaf drop, so that new sugar will continue to accumulate in the berries. Sometimes, it is required that protection measures be initiated during very cold temperature events during the winter on perennial tree and vine crops. Very often, only a couple of degrees rise in air temperature is sufficient to minimize cold damage, even in December or January.

The objective of any crop frost protection system is to keep plant tissues above their critical temperatures. The critical temperature is defined as the temperature at which tissues (cells) will be killed. Critical temperatures will vary with the stage of development and range from well below $0°F$ in midwinter to near $32°F$ in the spring, and they are strongly influenced by general weather patterns for seven to 14 days preceding the cold temperature event. They are most commonly reported for the 10%, 50% and 90% mortality levels.

Knowledge of the current critical temperatures and the latest weather forecast for air and dew point temperatures are important because they tell the producer how necessary heating may be at any stage of development and how much of a temperature increase should be required to protect the crop.

Use of water for frost protection in *V. vinifera* blocks is usually not recommended because of the need to carefully manage soil water levels. Under-canopy sprinkling systems are usually not an option; however, overhead sprinkling (at 70-80 gpm/acre) can provide the highest level of frost protection of any of the methods currently used, if the application rates are sufficient and uniform. It is also the only technique that does not rely on the inversion layer for its effectiveness, and it is the only method that can provide some protection under windy conditions (with some risk!). Disadvantages of the method include the very large water requirements, ice loadings, and severe damage potential in the event of a water application system failure. In addition, sprinkling systems cannot be used during winter cold protection activities.

Wind machines or "fans" rely totally on the strength of the temperature inversion for their effectiveness in warming the vineyard. The large propeller pulls warmer air from higher layers in the inversion and mixes it through the vineyard. This removes the cold air boundary layers around the buds/leaves and replaces it with warmer air. They can also be used to push cold air out of a vineyard.

The placement of multiple wind machines must be carefully coordinated to maximize the aerial extent and net effectiveness. Wind machines have been found to work well with properly placed propane or oil orchard heaters. This combination is probably the most appropriate for wintertime cold protection in vineyards.

There is no perfect method for field protection of crops against cold, but quite often combinations of methods are advantageous. The capacity of any system or combined systems will always be exceeded at some point. In addition, a well-maintained and calibrated frost monitoring (thermometers and alarms) network will always be required.

BIBLIOGRAPHY

Bucks, D.A, O.F. French, F.S. Nakayama and D.D. Fangmeier, 1985. Trickle irrigation management for grape production. Vol 1. Proceedings Third International Drip/Trickle Irrigation Congress. Fresno, CA. American Society of Agricultural Engineers. pp 204-211.

Department of Water Resources, State of California, 1974. Vegetative water use in California. Bull. No. 113-3. Sacramento, CA.

Doorenbos, J. and W.O. Pruitt, 1984. Guidelines for predicting crop water requirements. Irrigation and Drainage Paper 24. 2nd Edition. Food and Agriculture Organization of the United Nations. Rome. 144 pp.

Evans, R.G., 1994. Designing Multipurpose Water Application Systems. Proceedings 1994 Pacific Northwest Fruit School: *Tree Fruit Irrigation*. Chapter 16. Wenatchee, WA, February 15-17. Published by Good Fruit Grower, Yakima, WA. pp. 171-192.

Evans, R.G., 1992. Water use of wine grapes. Proc. WA State Grape Soc. Ann. Mtg., Yakima, WA. 22:23-33.

Evans, R.G., S.E. Spayd, R.L. Wample, and M.W. Kroeger, 1990. Water Requirements and Irrigation Management of Vitis Vinifera Grapes. Proc. of Third National Irrigation Symposium. October 28-Nov 1. ASAE. Phoenix, AZ. pp. 154-161.

Evans, R.G., M.W. Kroeger, and M.O. Mahan, 1991. Installation and operation of large drainage lysimeters. Proc. Internat. Symp. on Lysimetry. ASCE. Honolulu, HI. July 23-25. pp. 388-396.

Evans, R.G., S.E. Spayd, R.L. Wample, M.W. Kroeger, and M.O. Mahan. 1993. Water use of *Vitus vinifera* grapes in Washington. Agr. Water Mgmt. 23(1993):109-124.

Grimes, D.W. and L.E. Williams, 1990. Irrigation Effects on Plant Water Relations and Productivity of Thompson Seedless Grapevines. *Crop Science* 30:255-260.

James, L.G., J.M. Erpenbeck, D.L. Bassett, and J.E. Middleton, 1982. Irrigation requirements for Washington—estimates and methodology. Research Bulletin XB 0925. Agricultural Research Center, Washington State University, Pullman, WA. 37 pp.

Kottwitz, A.E., 1984. An irrigation management program for center-pivot irrigated wine grapes in South-Central Washington. Unpublished M.S. thesis. Agricultural Engineering Department, Washington State University, Pullman, WA. 103 pp.

McCarthy, M.G., 1981. Irrigation of grapevines with sewage effluent. I Effects on yield and petiole composition. Amer. J. Enol Vitic. 32(3):189-186.

Peacock W.L., L.P. Christensen, and H.L. Andris, 1987. Development of a drip irrigation schedule for average-canopy vineyards in the San Joaquin Valley. Amer. J. Enol. Vitic. 38(2):113-119.

Powers, J.R., C.W. Nagel, E.L. Proebsting, and M. Ahmedullah, 1979. Evaluation of selected vineyard sites in Washington State. Washington State University Ag. Res. Center Circ. XB 0908. Pullman, WA. 12 pp.

Rollin, H., S. Meriaux, and D. Boubals, 1981. Sur l'irrigation de la vigne dans le midi de al France. Progres Agricole et Viticole. 98(9):447-459.

Van Rooyen, F.C., 1980. The water requirements of table grapes. The Deciduous Fruit Grower (Die Sagtevrugteboer). South Africa. March. pp 100-106.

Van Zyl, J.L. and L. van Huyssteen, 1988. Irrigation systems—their role in water requirements and the performance of grapevines. S. Afr. J. Enol. Vitic. 9(2):3-8.

Williams, L.E., Personal communication, 1990. University of California, Kearney Field Station, Parlier, CA.

Williams, L.E. and M.A. Matthews, 1990. Grapevine. In: *Irrigation of Agricultural Crops*. Edited by B. A. Stewart and D. R. Nielsen. American Society of Agronomy Monograph No. 30. pp 1019-1055.

Winkler, A.J., J.A. Cook, W.M. Kliewer, and L.A. Lider, 1974. *General Viticulture*. University of California Press, Berkeley. 710 pp.

Water Relations and Irrigation Management of Wine Grapes

Robert L. Wample
Washington State University
Irrigated Agriculture Research and Extension Center
Prosser, Washington

Understanding plant water relations and soil water management are essential elements in our ability to use irrigation to produce consistent yields and high quality crops. Additionally, this understanding will allow us to use irrigation management to control plant growth more efficiently and therefore economically produce these crops. Finally, as we face rising competition for water, and as the major consumer of water in the western United States, agriculture will be under increasing pressure to reduce its water consumption.

FUNCTIONS OF WATER IN PLANTS

First, and perhaps most importantly, water is a major constituent of the plant cell protoplasm. The protoplasm is composed of the solution contained within the cell membrane and is referred to as the living part of the cell.

Vital plant functions such as photosynthesis, protein synthesis, and respiration take place in the protoplasm. These and many other processes that constitute "life" contribute to the ability of plants to grow and produce new structures, such as leaves, roots, and fruit.

Water also serves as the solvent for nutrient (fertilizer) uptake and the solvent in which the important chemical reactions that define life occur. In many cases, water may actually take part in these chemical reactions. One of the reactions that water takes part in, and is unique to plants, is photosynthesis, which results in the release of oxygen. Water is also a product of some reactions such as respiration.

Water is the principle component that imparts turgidity to plant cells. Lack of plant cell turgidity results in the characteristic "wilting," seen in plants under water stress. Turgidity is the result of the internal pressure caused by the combination of water and solutes inside of the cell pushing against the cell wall. Turgidity results from the accumulation of solutes such as sugars, amino acids, nutrients, proteins, and other complex molecules within the cell membrane, which tends to keep these compounds in the cell, while water moves freely across the cell membrane. The free movement of water across the cell membrane, and the chemical tendency of things to move from areas of high concentration to low concentration, cause water outside of the cell, where it is relatively pure and therefore highly concentrated, to move into the cell. The contents of the cell are prevented from leaking out by the membrane characteristics.

As the cell fills up with these solutes, water pressure is applied to the cell membrane in a manner similar to putting more air into a balloon. Surrounding this combination of cell membrane and protoplasm, which is referred to as the protoplast, is a cell wall that provides rigidity and structure to plant cells. The cell wall is made up of many small fibers called microfibrils that interact with one another and are partially held in place by other substances that are deposited as the cell ages.

As the pressure inside of the protoplast increases, it has the potential of stretching the cell wall, and, as such, the cell grows. As more water moves into the cell, the concentration of the proteins, sugars, etc., declines, and the concentration of water increases and reduces the driving force for more water to enter the cell. Furthermore, the resistance of the cell wall to the pressure caused by the expanding protoplast also restricts water entry into the protoplast. At the point where there is no net increase in the water content of the cell, the cell is said to be fully turgid.

Any change in the contents of the cell, such as an increase in sugars from photosynthesis, will result in an imbalance and stimulate additional movement of water into the cell. Another factor that would stimulate water movement into the cell would be a change in the resistance of the cell wall. For instance, if some of the "bonds" between the fibers were broken, this would allow more water to move into the cell. As more water moves into the cell in response to the loosening of the cell wall, there will be an increase in the cell size, and cell growth will have occurred.

Water is also responsible for maintaining leaf and fruit temperatures below air temperature through evaporative cooling. As the energy absorbed by leaves and fruit is transferred to water molecules, it increases the motion of the water molecules until they can break the bonds with other water molecules and go from a liquid to a gaseous state. The absorption of this large amount of energy to cause this transition helps maintain the temperature of well-irrigated plants one to two degrees or more below the air temperature. This is an important function of water in plants since many other physiological and metabolic processes that contribute to good plant growth and fruit production are temperature dependent and are inhibited by high temperatures.

PLANT WATER STATUS

Plant water status depends mainly on two factors, the rate of water supply and the rate of water loss. A major factor that influences the rate of water supply to a plant is the energy required to move water from the soil into the plant. Water in soils is generally considered to exist in either a relatively "plant accessible" form held between soil particles, and a less accessible form where the water molecules are held by attractive forces to soil particles. This is primarily associated with the size and aggregation of the soil particles. Very fine clay soils, although they can hold more water than sandy soils, "hold" the water more tightly and are said to have a higher soil moisture tension. This is because there are smaller spaces between soil particles and a much greater surface area of the clay particles to which the water molecules are strongly attracted.

Soil temperature can also influence the availability of soil water. Temperature affects the overall activity of water molecules in the soil and their likelihood of going between the liquid and vapor phases and therefore being redistributed in the soil profile. However, soil temperatures do not fluctuate widely below the top ten to twelve inches, so this has little effect on soil water availability for deep-rooted, permanent crops such as grapevines.

The rate of water supply to a plant is also affected by root distribution. Root distribution can be influenced by numerous factors, including irrigation method and scheduling, soil compaction and restricted layers, root health, and the growth characteristics of each plant species, cultivar, or rootstock. Plant nutrition and other cultural practices such as deep cultivation and ripping can influence root distribution and function and therefore affect water supply to the plant.

RATE OF WATER LOSS

The rate of water loss from plants is determined by a number of factors, including the level of solar radiation, air temperature, relative humidity, leaf area per plant, crop height, and crop density. Solar radiation has both direct and indirect effects on water loss. The direct effect is associated with air, soil, and plant temperature, while the indirect effect is through photosynthesis.

As sunlight increases up to near full sunlight (2,000 micromoles per square meter per second), the rate of photosynthesis increases, thus causing the stomata on the leaves to open. Stomata are specialized pairs of cells on the leaf's outer surface (epidermis) that, through changes in turgor, regulate the rate of gas exchange between the leaf and atmosphere. Hence, as the stomates open under increasing sunlight, more water is lost to the atmosphere (transpiration).

Air temperature affects the rate of water loss by influencing the relative humidity and therefore the concentration gradient from the leaf to the atmosphere. The relative humidity inside a leaf on a well-watered plant is assumed to be very close to 100%. The amount of water that can be present in a given volume of air increases as the temperature increases and thus reduces the relative humidity. The greater the difference between the internal leaf relative humidity and that of the atmosphere, the greater the transpiration rate. Clearly, the number and degree of opening of stomates on a leaf will have a direct effect on water loss.

Plant height and density influence the rate of water loss through their effects on the number of leaves directly exposed to the atmosphere at the lowest relative humidity. It is relatively easy to see how increasing the number of plants per acre could reduce the water loss by individual plants, while increasing the total water used by the crop. Factors such as pruning method (cane versus spur), training system (cordon versus head trained), and trellis system (bilateral cordon versus Scott-Henry) can change the degree of leaf exposure and height of vines and therefore water use also.

TERMINOLOGY USED TO INDICATE STATUS OF WATER AVAILABILITY

Attempts to define and quantify the energy status of water have resulted in the development of some conventions and terms that are now used universally. Based on this, the energy status of water is referred to as water potential. The water potential of pure water at sea level and at the same temperature of the sample to be evaluated is said to be equal to zero. Since the energy status of water is dependent upon its concentration, anything that results in a reduction of the purity and therefore concentration of water, has the effect of reducing the water potential, which results in a negative value. Hence, dissolved substances in water or complex solutions such as occur in plant cells, have negative water potentials.

In addition, a low relative humidity, which means a low concentration of water molecules relative to the temperature and total volume of air being considered, results in negative water potentials. A basic chemical principle states that molecules can only move from a higher concentration or energy level to a lower concentration or energy level. Thus, if pure liquid water were present in a room with low relative humidity, we would expect the water to evaporate (i.e., go from a higher to lower energy state). Likewise, available water in the soil will have a higher water potential than water in root cells and will have a tendency to move into the roots.

The units that are typically used to quantify water potential are pressure units such as pounds per square inch (psi), and bars or megapascals (MPa). One bar is equal to 14.5 psi or 0.1 MPa. Since pure water is assigned a value of zero, solutions will have negative values such as -0.1 MPa, which would be equal to -1.0 bar.

Understanding these basic conventions and chemical principles helps us understand and predict the movement of water in the soil and plant system. Therefore, since under normal agricultural conditions, water moves from the soil to the plant and out to the atmosphere, we would expect a more negative water potential for the atmosphere than in the leaf, which is more negative than in the stem, etc. The magnitude of the difference between the soil and atmosphere water potentials will determine the rate of water movement in the soil-plant-atmosphere system.

IRRIGATION MANAGEMENT

Whether it is because we would like to maintain or increase the yield of our grapevines or we are concerned with the production of higher quality grapes, irrigation and irrigation management is a frequent topic of discussion in viticultural regions around the world. Irrigation is now being considered as an acceptable practice, even in areas where irrigation has historically been prohibited. Research throughout these viticultural regions has provided variable results that appear to be heavily dependent on the local environmental conditions. Despite the fact the studies are inconclusive, they have provided some insights regarding the conditions under which irrigation is needed or is at least beneficial.

With a basic understanding of the soil-plant-atmosphere water relationships, it is possible to begin estimating the availability and use of water by grapevines. A convenient way to think of the system is to think of it as a bank account, where deposits and withdrawals are made. Since we recognize that differing soil types have different water-holding capacities, and that the soil and rooting depth also influence the amount of water available, we must recognize initially what the maximum deposit or bank balance is for any given site and grapevine combination.

For instance, shallow sandy soils may have a field capacity (maximum bank balance) of no more than one to two acre-inches of available water, while a deep silt-loam soil may hold six to eight inches or more of available water. Field capacity refers to the amount of water held by a soil after all excess water has drained out in response to gravity.

Knowing this information is critical for making decisions regarding the frequency and duration of irrigation cycles. For example, applying three to four acre-inches of water to the sandy soil would not be an efficient use of water, while it could also result in leaching of fertilizers out of the root zone and potentially into groundwater sources. It is also important to know the infiltration rate for the soil types in your vineyard. This refers to the rate at which water can enter the soil without surface runoff. Exceeding the infiltration rate results in inefficient use of water, and depending upon the degree to which it is exceeded, it might result in soil erosion or other problems.

In general, for maximum plant growth, the soil moisture should be kept as close to field capacity as possible. Thus, application of sufficient water on a daily basis to account for the loss of water due to evaporation from the soil and transpiration by the grapevines and any other plants in the vineyard, would promote maximum vegetative growth. This, of course, assumes there are no other limiting factors such as fertilizers or pests and diseases acting on the vines. As for vine growth, this also assumes that the competition with weeds or cover crops is minimized or eliminated.

Estimating the amount of water being consumed requires that we understand the rate of withdrawal by the vines and surrounding cover crop, if present. Cover crops vary considerably with respect to rooting depth and water consumption. Deep-rooted cover crops are generally avoided to prevent competition with the grapevines for water and nutrients. In drip irrigated vineyards of central Washington, the cover crop often goes dormant or dies back during the summer due to lack of water and hence has little effect on water use. In sprinkler-irrigated vineyards where cover crops are planted annually, they are often controlled chemically, starting in early June, to reduce their water use. In both cases mentioned above, it is estimated that cover crops increase water use by about 10% to 20%.

In sprinkler-irrigated vineyards with permanent cover crops, there are varying estimates of water use, due primarily to the aggressiveness of the cover crop. Values derived from previous research probably overestimate the amount of water currently used today because of the increasing application of irrigation practices to control canopy size.

Grapevine water use has been estimated by using large containers, lysimeters (10 ft. x 12 ft. x 6 ft., W x L x D) where the amount of water applied was measured with a meter, the amount of water in the soil was measured with a neutron probe soil moisture sensor, and any excess water moving through the soil profile was extracted and measured with a vacuum system (Evans et al. 1993). With these three values, it is possible to calculate the amount of water used by the grapevines. This research was carried out using full irrigation replacement and hence resulted in high levels of vine growth. The consequence of this research was the development of a set of values referred to as grapevine crop coefficients (K_c). These values *(Figure 1)* represent the fractional water use (evapotranspiration) of a reference crop which is typically a well watered, mowed, grass area referred to as ETp. To calculate grapevine daily water use (DWU), the ETp value is multiplied by the K_c for grapevines (DWU = ETp x K_c).

ETp values are typically available from several sources such as the U.S. Weather Service and public agriculture weather systems. Grapevine crop coefficients have been developed in several different locations in addition to the ones by Evans et al. 1993 (Grimes and Williams, 1994; Doorenbos and Pruitt, 1975) and reflect the development of leaf surface area and vine water demand as the growing season progresses. Since they represent the fraction or percentage of the potential evapo-transpiration, their values are typically less than one. Because of the variability in development in different years, they are usually associated with accumulated growing degree-days (GDD) rather than the day of the year.

The base temperature used to calculate GDD accumulation for grapevines is 50°F (10°C). In northern temperate climates, the usual date to begin this calculation is April 1. The calculation of daily GDD is based on the daily maximum plus the daily minimum temperature divided by two, minus the base temperature (50°F), or [(max °F + min °F)/2] –50°F. For example, the GDD accumulated for a day with 90°F and 60°F maximum and minimum temperatures, respectively, would be 25 GDD: [(90 + 60)/2] –50 = 25.

The use of GDD helps overcome year-to-year variation in vine development, since vine growth is heavily influenced by temperature. Figure 1 shows the K_c developed for mature

FIGURE I

The K_c developed for fully irrigated, mature vines of Cabernet Sauvignon, White Riesling, and Chenin Blanc grown in Washington State. There was no cover crop present in this study. *(See Evans et al. 1993, for more information.)*

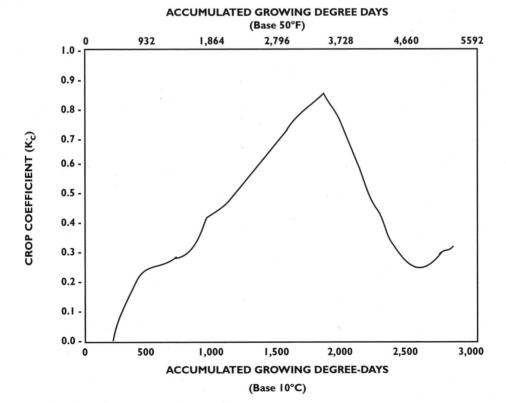

vines of Cabernet Sauvignon, White Riesling, and Chenin Blanc grown in Washington. Early in the season, the K_c is low due to the small leaf area and resulting low vine water use. The K_c approaches 1.0 as the canopy reaches its maximum development in July and August in northern climates and earlier in more southern locations. For instance, the K_c at 1652 GDD°F from Figure 1 is about 0.8, and if the ETp was 0.2 inch, the DWU would equal 0.16 inch.

The availability and use of computers make these calculations and record-keeping easy and facilitate better water management than in the past. Knowing the available water in the soil and the rate of water use makes it possible to schedule irrigation when desired, before vine water stress develops. These calculations must also take into consideration any rainfall that occurs during the irrigation intervals.

In considering rainfall, it is important to recognize that not all rainfall reaches the vine's root zone. Some reasons for this include interception of the rainfall by cover crops and vine canopy, light rainfall followed by sufficient evaporative demand to prevent movement into the soil, insufficient rainfall to fill more than the upper inch or two of the soil profile, and poor infiltration due to surface barriers, and/or rates of rainfall that are too high for the infiltration rate of the soil and result in high runoff.

The delivery capacity of the irrigation system needs to be factored into any decision to irrigate. This is particularly true for a large vineyard where it would be unlikely that it could all be irrigated simultaneously. In a hypothetical situation, if it takes 48 hours to apply the necessary amount of water to bring one-third of the vineyard to the desired soil moisture level, it will take six days to complete the irrigation cycle. On deeper soils with higher water-holding capacity, this length of time would present less of a problem since they have a greater "buffering capacity" than shallow soils. However, during high evaporative demand conditions, on shallow soils with low water-holding capacity, the inability to keep pace with the rate of water use could mean that some vines would experience significant water stress. When this occurs, it would suggest that the irrigation design was insufficient to meet the peak demand of this vineyard farming operation. This situation often develops when an initial irrigation system is used to service additional acreage that is developed at a later date.

Another factor that needs to be considered is that as differential irrigation practices are applied and canopy development is reduced, there will be a reduction in grapevine water use. Assuming that the irrigation practice used and the environmental conditions permit, it would be desirable to control canopy development for wine grape production at 36 to 48 inches of shoot growth. Preferably, most of the change in canopy development, compared to a fully irrigated vine, will take place about 30 days after full bloom. This will provide, as discussed above, adequate leaf area for fruit and vine maturation. Thus, to adjust irrigation practices for a smaller canopy, the K_c can be reduced at the time when it is clear that shoot growth has declined. The amount of reduction should be in proportion to the amount of reduction in canopy size compared to a fully irrigated vine. This is due to the fact that the K_c shown in Figure 1 is based on vines receiving full irrigation. Using this approach to adjusting the K_c also allows for variations in canopy development occurring in different years and in response to different management practices. It is also possible to make adjustments according to the cultivar being grown and the desired yield and fruit characteristics.

Knowing when and how much irrigation will be required are important factors to consider in choosing the method of irrigation. Vineyards planted on hillsides or with rolling terrain are not amenable to furrow or flood irrigation practices. Soils with low infiltration rates and with a significant slope also present runoff problems for overhead sprinkler systems with high delivery rates. Drip irrigation can accommodate all of these situations, but has a higher initial capital investment cost and is generally considered to require a higher level of management that must be taken into consideration. Additional factors that need to be considered when deciding on an irrigation system are water quality, filtration requirements, system automation, and local availability of equipment, supplies, and support. Because of the number of variables involved, it is recommended that vineyard managers contact local irrigation design and equipment companies for recommendations tailored to their vineyard.

In the event such services are not available locally, vineyard managers are advised to seek help from county Extension specialists, land-grant university faculty, and professional organizations such as the American Society of Agricultural Engineers. In addition, several trade journals offer annual issues that list producers and suppliers of equipment and services.

HOW TO USE THIS INFORMATION

To effectively and efficiently use the information and strategies discussed in this chapter, the first step is to clearly define the goals for your vineyard. This should include the cultivars to be grown, and the tonnage and quality to be achieved. Once these goals are defined, it is essential that the necessary information about the vineyard site be collected to allow for a full evaluation of the factors (soil characteristics, slope, elevation, level and seasonal nature of rainfall) that will influence the availability and use of water by grapevines.

Trellis type and vine training practices should also be considered, especially if there will be significant differences within the vineyard, or from the systems used to develop vine water use values. This could also include significant increases in vine density (e.g., 1,200 versus 700 vines per acre).

Once this information has been accumulated and fully evaluated, it is essential to develop a working knowledge of the terms, equipment, measurements, and calculations necessary to estimate soil moisture, vine water use, and irrigation levels for the vineyard. This knowledge can be used, if necessary, to choose the irrigation method and refine its design, to ensure that the system is capable of meeting the seasonal peak demand

and avoiding undesired vine water stress. To effectively manage vineyard water, a complete understanding of the irrigation system must be combined with the recognition that a higher level of management is being applied to the vineyard. Acknowledging this dictates that more time may be required to achieve the desired results. As mentioned earlier, the increased management should lead to reduced costs for training and canopy management procedures, perhaps reduced investment costs for trellis systems, reduced pest management costs, more efficient use of water and fertilizers, and improved fruit quality.

Grapevine irrigation, especially of European grapes *(Vitis vinifera)*, can be accomplished without the information and effort described here, primarily because of the rather remarkable drought tolerance of these plants. However, as competition for resources (both natural and otherwise), consumer acceptance (price and quality) increases, and the public demands that we become more responsible in our farming practices, we must look for ways to be more efficient while producing more and a higher quality product, and at the same time reducing any potential negative impacts on the environment. Grapevine irrigation management in eastern Washington has the potential for achieving these goals and is a component of the emerging overall management philosophy referred to as precision farming.

REFERENCES

Williams, L.E., N.K. Dokoozlian, and R.L. Wample. 1994. "Grape." In: *Handbook of Environmental Physiology of Fruit Crops,* Volume I, Temperate Crops. Edited by B. Schaffer and P.C. Andersen. CRC Press, Boca Raton, FL.

Wolpert, J.A., M.A. Walker and E. Walker. 1992. *Rootstock Seminar: A Worldwide Perspective.* American Society of Enology and Viticulture, Davis, CA. 84 pp.

Evans, R.G., S.E. Spayd, R.L Wample, M.W. Kroeger, and M.O. Mahan. 1993. "Water use of *Vitis vinifera* grapes in Washington." *Agric. Water Mgmt.* 23: 109-124.

Grimes, D.W. and L.E. Williams. 1990. "Irrigation effects on plant water relations and productivity of Thompson Seedless grapevines." *Crop Sci.* 30: 255-260.

Doorenbos, J. and W.O. Pruitt. 1977. "Guidelines for predicting crop water requirements." Irrigation and drainage paper 24. Food and Agriculture Organization of the United Nations, Rome, Italy. 144 pp.

Grape Insect Pest Management for the Next Century

Wyatt Cone
Entomologist, Washington State University
Irrigated Agriculture Research and Extension Center
Prosser, Washington

The Pacific Northwest region of the United States is one of the finest areas in the world for premium grape production. We don't get the long, sustained summer heat of locations across the southern tier of states, nor do we get the long, sustained cold winters of the north-central or northeastern states. Our region may be characterized as having warm days and cool nights, and, for the most part, our winters are relatively mild.

In addition to good soils, access to irrigation, and general freedom from damaging summer storms, we have relatively few insect and mite pests compared to other regions of the United States or other areas in the world. This chapter speaks about some of these factors, makes some comparisons with other areas, and projects what I see as the strengths and weaknesses in the future for grape pest management.

CHEMICALS
Existing Compounds and Pest Problems

For several generations, insecticides have been a relatively cheap, available, first line of defense for most arthropod pests of grapes. We have had an adequate number of compounds upon which to draw to reach a reasonable fit between the pest to be controlled and the cost to do the job. Put another way, pesticides have been relatively inexpensive, and we haven't had to seriously consider cost.

Often the equipment and the operator have cost more than the chemical, if considered on an acre or hourly basis. In more recent years, the chemical may have represented several times the cost of the equipment and the operator. There is every indication that this trend will continue as we go into the next century.

Let me cite a few examples to illustrate this point. For about 30 years, we (the grape industry) relied on a parathion-oil combination applied as a delayed dormant spray for control of grape mealybug. The U.S. Environmental Protection Agency (EPA) banned the use of ethyl parathion in December 1993.

For several years, we essentially did without chemical control of grape mealybug, since the remaining compounds were marginally effective or, in the case of malathion, had to be used at 2.5 times the rate of parathion and were more expensive on a per-pound basis.

Finally, we were able to get Lorsban (chlorpyrifos) on a Section 18 emergency exemption from registration, and it ultimately received a special local needs (24c) registration.

With the passage of the Food Quality Protection Act by Congress in August 1996, all the organophosphate and carbamate compounds are scheduled to be reviewed. The anticipated result of the review process will be numerous losses of uses and ultimately, if that process goes past the point of economic profitability, the loss of these compounds. The companies manufacturing these chemicals will protect those uses which are profitable and give up the rest. Overseas markets will be possible outlets.

The fungicide Captan was banned because of possible cancer-producing effects in laboratory mice. Captan was used for sooty mold and mildew control with a crop tolerance of 200 ppm. The dermal and chronic toxicity was very low—about equal to table salt or aspirin. The fungicides to replace Captan are much more expensive and, in some cases, considerably more toxic.

The Future of "Hard" Pesticides

Where does that leave us? In the short term (1-2 years), we have a few compounds left.

For example, if a vineyard has a black vine weevil problem, we can still use carbofuran (Furdan), and I would encourage anyone to take care of a weevil problem this season because the means may not be there the following year. I can almost guarantee it won't be there in the next century.

There are a few compounds coming down the pipeline, and there probably will continue to be a few for many years to come. There is a major difference however. In the past, where a compound like the organophosphates cost $5 to $10 per pound, the new ones are likely to be $500 to $1,000 per pound. However, with these new compounds the use rates will be much lower, which reduces the cost somewhat to the grower on a per-acre basis. The cost still will be several times (3-5 times) the old cost per acre. It also means a grower must be much more careful over a range of factors, which vary from purchasing to the calibration of equipment.

One great advantage of the new "hard" pesticides is that they generally represent new families of chemistry which will be very helpful in the management of insect pests developing resistance to pesticides. As our list of available compounds becomes progressively shorter, we must think about alternating chemicals and try to avoid using the same one two or three times per season year after year. It is almost a "Catch 22"—fewer and fewer compounds with greater demand placed on them.

The Future of "Soft" Pesticides

When I think of "soft" pesticides, I think of oils, soaps, botanical-based compounds, the use of insect diseases (Bt), or insect growth regulators. The use of attractants and repellants probably should be included here as well. These are compounds that generally are of low toxicity, have no particular deleterious effects such as carcinogenicity (cancer), mutogenicity (gene mutation), or oncogenicity (tumor producing). The cloud that looms on the horizon now is, "do these have any effect on endocrine systems?" That will likely be a very big question in the next century. Today, we recognize the complexity of the question and acknowledge we have little or no data to address the question. Consequently, we (the public or society in general) have pushed this off into the future, and political activists are not actively demanding that "something be done."

I think we will see increasing use of soft pesticides in the next century. I have to say 'up front' that they are less effective than compounds we have used in the past—in some cases, much less effective. It means we must be more diligent in assessing the problem, and it probably means five or six applications instead of one or two. Cost, again, is going to be a factor. Take soaps as an example—in general we are talking one to two gallons per acre maybe three to four times per season at a cost of $40 to $50 per gallon. I think you can see that the manager must be very careful when making decisions.

NEW OR INTRODUCED PESTS

I believe the grape industry of the Pacific Northwest has fairly simple insect and mite pest problems. I say that when I compare this region to other grape-growing regions of the United States or other grape-growing regions of the world. I would like to see our grape industry keep it that way.

One good defense is to be aware of the presence of a new pest—in other words, something you haven't seen before. It may be a native insect or mite coming onto the crop in some of the new areas being developed, or it may be a new introduction from outside this region. The best way to gain awareness is monitoring. Be watchful. Read and study about pests that potentially could be serious problems. Know what they look like and what their injury looks like. In this sense, education is part of the defense.

Another area or subject to keep in mind is quarantine. As I mentioned earlier, we have relatively few pests compared to other regions of the United States or other regions of the world.

We don't have grape berry moth—a serious pest in the Northeast; we don't have several important moth pests found in California. We don't have grape root borer found in Missouri and Arkansas. We don't have several moth pests found in France that probably would do fine if they were introduced here. It's hard to say what might come from the Southern Hemisphere—South Africa, Chile, Australia, etc. The point is, we don't want them. Consequently, a system of legal quarantines with official inspection of plant materials to some set standard may be useful in the future. We have some quarantines on the books already.

CULTURAL PRACTICES

Farmers have always been in a position of trying to find ways to become more efficient, cut costs, and increase profitability. As we continue to move away from hard pesticides and towards new, innovative management practices, we will adapt and use a number of different cultural practices. This subject area could include the topics I've listed here (there are some I haven't included), but may also include practices yet to be developed. Such subjects as soil erosion, soil chemistry, plant nutrition, utilization of solar energy, etc. may fit in this area. We will be looking more and more at the "fine" points.

Drip irrigation as a cultural practice has impact on entomological problems. In one sense, it may be a valuable delivery system. On the other hand, we may find that problems like mites and leafhoppers become more important when we grow grapes under very close management schemes. I think about managing canopy vs. crop load or plant vigor by regulation of water. In either of these cases,

if we lose control of leaf pests, we may find ourselves in a position where we don't have enough foliage to mature the crop or we lose the quality factors. Otherwise, we would choose to maximize tonnage, if quality were not a desired goal. You can see that drip irrigation and canopy management are closely intertwined.

Cover crops are of increasing interest and I believe will continue to be of interest for decades to come. We have just begun to scratch the surface. We have a lot to learn about specific cover crop/site interactions. From an entomological point of view, there are many possibilities, ranging from crops that repel pests to those that are preferred hosts compared to grapes (a trap crop). Some may have a direct toxic effect on pests when used as a green manure crop (example: glucosinolates from the family Brassica). This is an area that will require research experience. I sense a problem if we try to overgeneralize, i.e., if we move to general recommendations based on a good cover crop experience here and there. Other factors may be responsible for what we attribute to cover crop.

BIOLOGICAL CONTROL

Biological control, along with soft pesticides and cultural practices, will have some things to offer. I've listed entomopathogenic nematodes because it's an area with which we have some experience. In some cases, we have had marvelous results; in other cases, not so good. Ralph Berry at Oregon State University is doing some excellent pioneering work. A former graduate student Ludger Wennemann did some fundamental work with species interaction and the mechanics of how to use them in vineyards. Again, this kind of work takes time and experience, and we need to resist the temptation to overgeneralize.

Disease is an area where much good can be done in the future. We have diseases such as Bt *(Bacillus thuriengiensis)*, with all its strains and subspecies that are very effective against certain pests. Biotechnologists have incorporated Bt genes into cotton and potato germplasm. This would seem like the answer to end all pest problems, but no sooner has this dramatic achievement entered the field than researchers find larvae that have mechanisms for survival. However, this should not derail our interest in diseases of insect pests. To the contrary, we need to continue the search for bacteria, viruses, viroids, mycoplasma, and other naturally-occurring pathogens that might be adapted for use in grape insect pest management.

The biological control agents, the parasitoids and predators, are probably more familiar to you. We can cite examples where these agents already benefit us. I think of *Anagrus* wasps as parasites of grape leafhopper eggs or western predatory mites as predators of mite pests on grapes. And there are others. Again, we need to determine how parasitoids and predators can best be used in grape pest management in this region. One thing to keep in mind is: if we get a new pest in from some other region, an effort should be made to go to the region of origin and seek natural enemies. Often the pest makes the jump and leaves its natural enemies behind.

MANAGEMENT STRATEGIES AND TACTICS

I've listed some words here that will become more familiar to each of you, if they aren't already. These are economic thresholds and economic injury levels. This is the language of integrated pest management (IPM). I've listed sampling first because it is of paramount importance. None of this works without good sampling strategy and tactics.

Basically, we follow insect numbers through time. Insect numbers may have an equilibrium position below an economic threshold (ET). Occasionally, numbers rise above that threshold and approach the economic injury level (EIL). At that time, some management tactic must be employed in order to avoid economic loss, i.e., when the pest population rises above the EIL.

RESEARCH BASE

Progress in the management of insect pests in the next century will be no better than the research base upon which strategies and tactics are developed.

Public-funded research in entomology and agriculture in general is drying up fast. The American public has provided support for and received the benefits of agricultural research for about 100 years.

What is happening to agricultural research? Some of it is being taken over by private companies. I strongly support this as being truly American, but what is happening is that those areas that can generate a quick

TABLE I

Summary: a statement for the future of grape insect pest management.

	Strengths	Weaknesses
"hard" chemicals	there will be some with low mammalian toxicity	expensive (4x-10x, due to developmental costs, not expensive chemistry)
"soft" pesticides	reduced hazards to humans	• expensive • more applications • companies will have development risks—how to protect their product
new pests	we will be better aware and, hopefully, can respond (eradication procedures)	monitoring/enforcement
cultural practices	these will just be • good farming practices • aided by advances in technology	at best a partial answer to pest problems
biological control	• in some cases, very stable • low maintenance costs	difficulty in finding practical examples (cause & effect)
management	• general increase in monitoring • an aid in making informed decisions	slight increased cost
research base	• some very rapid progress in certain areas	• loss of long-term basic research • can not be replaced quickly

profit grow rapidly, make their contribution (and profit), and move on as the product loses profitability. Very few are interested in long-term, sustained research that generates an information base which serves as the departure point for new developments. For those that have a sustained research program, the information is proprietary.

Some companies are engaged in basic research but not generally in areas that will benefit, say, the wine grape grower in Pasco, Washington. There is no money in developing parasitoids for grape mealybugs or determining which vetch species is the best when grown as a cover crop for Cabernet Sauvignon grapes on light, sandy soil. And yet such knowledge may be of considerable benefit and economic gain to the Washington grape industry.

I have no answer for this problem. I can only say I have great apprehension as I see the public agricultural research base decline. I know that the infusion of large amounts of money when outbreaks or epidemics occur in the future will not take the place of studying the interaction of crop with seasons when we seek true solutions to problems.

Epidemiology and Management of Grape Powdery Mildew

Gary G. Grove
Plant Pathologist, Washington State University
Tree Fruit Research and Extension Center
Wenatchee, Washington

Powdery mildew is caused by the fungus *Uncinula necator* and is the most serious disease of wine grapes in Washington State. Several severe epidemics, the most of recent of which occurred during 1995, have resulted in devastating losses in our wine industry. The disease is circumglobal—it can be severe anywhere that wine grapes are produced and is particularly problematic in the Pacific Northwest, Oregon, and California. Powdery mildew can have adverse effects on fruit yield and quality—wine quality can be affected when only three percent of berries are infected. Chardonnay, Chenin Blanc, and Cabernet Sauvignon are highly susceptible to powdery mildew, while White Riesling and Merlot are moderately susceptible.

SYMPTOMS AND SIGNS

The earliest symptoms on foliage are red chlorotic flecks or spots on the upper leaf surface. Later, an obvious white mealy coating develops on the foliage and may also be evident on berry surfaces and rachises. Infection of shoots results in a red blotchiness once canes become dormant. Small brown-black fungal fruiting bodies may be evident late in the season on older mildew colonies. These are called cleistothecia and represent the sexual phase of the mildew fungus life cycle.

EPIDEMIOLOGY

Plant disease epidemics occur under certain conditions, and they occur in phases. These phases include, but are not limited to, survival, dispersal, primary infection, incubation, dispersal, secondary infection, and dispersal. Each phase serves to increase the number of plants or plant organs infected. All of the phases are linked together like the links of a chain.

Approach disease control as if you were trying to break the links of the chain. Think of the epidemic progress as starting at bud break and going through the season. The spores that start the epidemic originate from the overwintering inoculum and are called primary inoculum. Keep in mind if we could eliminate that, or at least reduce the amount of it, anything that followed would be less severe.

If primary infections go uncontrolled, the spores produced travel in the wind to leaves where they produce more infections called secondary infections, which produce more spores, and more colonies, and thus, things rapidly get out of hand.

When you actually see the mildew, it is producing chains of spores. These blow in the wind to leaves and fruit and start their own colonies.

By the time you actually see this, the real damage occurred probably weeks, if not a month earlier. In other words, when you actually see the mildew, the infections have already occurred.

The actual white mildew that you see is secondary mildew. This is the phase responsible for the spread and increase in intensity of the epidemic.

SURVIVAL AND THE SEXUAL STAGE OF *UNCINULA NECATOR*

Sometimes, the fungus produces minute spherical structures known as cleistothecia. Cleistothecia are the sexual phase of the grape mildew fungus life cycle. In Washington, cleistothecia perennate the fungus over the winter. Inside cleistothecia, there are spore sacs (called asci) which produce the sexual spores. These spores are called ascospores. Cleistothecia are produced on the leaves and the fruit, beginning in August. They are blown by the wind or splashed by water into the bark of the vine. Some of them survive winter there, while smaller proportions survive in the leaf litter on the vineyard floor.

The time of cleistothecia formation depends a lot on when the infection first occurred and the temperatures after mildew is established in the vineyard. During 1997, we found very few in early August, but by the end of August, cleistothecia were numerous. In 1998, it was a month later. The extreme heat of late July and August was just too hot for the fungus. One thing we are investigating is late-season oil sprays to try to prevent the cleistothecia from forming. We know that if we prevent them from forming, the fungus cannot survive the winter. It is highly unlikely that we will be able to eliminate them entirely.

Cleistothecia need free water in order to burst open and liberate ascospores into the air. The water can be in the form of irrigation water or rainwater. When the cleistothecium gets wet, the spore sacs inside shoot the spores out into the air. These spores will land on young leaves and germinate to then produce a mildew colony. Therefore, the overwintering stage of the cleistothecia is what starts the epidemic, and the spores that actually start the epidemic are called primary inoculum or ascospores.

We have been studying survival and primary infection for several years. The percent of viable cleistothecia decreases rapidly during May and June. Prior to bud break, viability is high but essentially irrelevant because there is no tissue for the fungus to infect. We have found that the cleistothecia (some of them at least) survived the winter into April and very early May. The potential for spore release is highest right after the vines come out of dormancy. The fungus can also overwinter in buds, as it does in some areas of California. We have found no evidence of bud perennation in eastern Washington. It is the sexual stage (cleistothecia) that allows this fungus to survive the winter in our area. In that regard, powdery mildew in eastern Washington is epidemiologically similar to the disease in upstate New York and in some areas of California.

The sexual or cleistothecial stage is the primary inoculum source. It initiates epidemics in the spring, and because it is dependent upon free water, it is somewhat predictable. Cleistothecia must have free water in order for ascospore release to occur. Second, and perhaps most importantly, it is where genetic recombination occurs. The sexual stage is the primary source of genetic variability. This becomes very important because of the use of resistance-prone fungicides. The DMI or sterol-inhibiting fungicides that we have been using for 10 or 15 years are prone to resistance, as are some of the new fungicides that are coming onto the market. The faster the fungus becomes more genetically variable, the faster resistance will occur.

ASCOSPORE RELEASE AND PRIMARY INFECTION

We have looked at several models of ascospore release, one from California and one from New York. The one that seems to apply closely here is the Pearson model from New York, which uses parameters of 0.10 inch of rain at 50°F or greater between the phases of bud break and through the bloom period for spore release. In Washington, the moisture can be from rain or irrigation water. Once the above conditions have been met and spore release occurs, it has to be warmer than 46°F after spore release for infection to occur.

In our vineyard studies, we generally begin to detect secondary spores (conidia) about mid-June. In 1998, we had a Pearson primary infection event in early June when about .20 of an inch of rain fell. The average temperature was 65°F. We trapped some ascospores during that event, and about six days later, we started to trap conidia in the spore trap. The trapping of the secondary spores seven days after the primary spores were released fits with the incubation period of this disease, which is five or six days at these temperatures. This model appears to be relatively accurate, but it is not a cure-all.

SECONDARY MILDEW AND SECONDARY INFECTION

Once white mildew colonies are apparent on the leaves or on the fruit, the mildew is already into its secondary phase. The optimum temperature for infection by the spores produced by this phase is in the mid to high 70s and lower 80s. The spores will germinate in five hours when temperatures are in the high 70s. When temperatures are conducive, the incubation period (or the time from when the spore germinates to when you see the mildew) is five or six days. Low diffuse light and poor air movement favors the secondary stage. Because the mildews reproduce quickly and produce so many spores, they can rapidly develop fungicide resistance.

Fruit Infection

Infections that are noticed in mid to late summer are usually the result of infection events early in fruit development. Problems usually originate from wet weather, a poor spray program (meaning poor coverage or an ineffective compound), or a combination of those factors. On Concords, the highest level of infection occurs between prebloom and fruit set. With Chardonnay and Riesling, some susceptibility is retained all the way to midsummer. Some New York work has shown that the fruit of Chardonnay become relatively resistant about a month before reaching 8° Brix.

CULTURAL PRACTICES THAT CAN LOWER DISEASE PRESSURE

Cultural practices that favor good air circulation should be followed. This promotes drying and lowers the humidity, which in turn, lowers disease pressure. Also, the fungus is inhibited by sunlight; because of this, excess shading should be discouraged. The producer or field consultant should always keep in mind that excessive amounts of nitrogen will promote the production of succulent growth and increase disease pressure.

FUNGICIDE SPRAY PROGRAMS

In terms of powdery mildew fungicide usage, good coverage is absolutely critical. It is imperative that the grower use an effective compound and get adequate spray coverage.

The best time to be on your toes is very early in the season. There is now a lot of evidence that the phase between bud break and bloom is very critical. If mildew is not controlled at this stage, it can mean a summer full of headaches.

When you spray early, you hold down the number of leaves that become infected. This is critical because you keep the number of mildew colonies lower. The later sprays are what I would call "catch-up" sprays and serve to reduce the disease severity on the leaves that are already infected.

Obviously, you cannot start early and avoid your later sprays altogether, but the early sprays are very, very critical because if you keep it under control early, you are not going to have as much to deal with later as the epidemic progresses.

For years (particularly in tree fruit, and it seems to be the same way in grapes), a lot of our spray dollars have been spent during the later phases of mildew epidemics. In tree fruit, it used to be that a lot of people didn't worry about mildew until it was out of control. That is how we got into trouble with some of the fungicides we were using. Fungicides were applied when the disease was out of control, exposing a lot of fungal propagules to the chemicals, and selected propagules became less sensitive to the fungicides.

Spray Timings and Approaches

In terms of a spray approach, you need to start early to keep the colony number down. The immediate prebloom and first postbloom sprays are very, very critical. Part of the reason those are so critical is that you can have moisture, susceptible host tissue, and viable overwintering cleistothecia in the vineyard all at the same time. You have to protect young foliage from primary infection. Always be certain you are using effective materials, and always use labeled rates. If it calls for a range on the label, stay within that range, do not go above or below it. Always spray under good conditions. It is essential that you get good spray coverage.

FUNGICIDES

Sulfur compounds have been used against powdery mildews for years. Our most popular compounds are the DMI (sterol-inhibiting) fungicides, which include Rally, Procure, and Rubigan. There is a new class of compounds called strobilurins. The strobilurins are the compounds derived from wood-rotting fungi. They are systemic compounds and are relatively effective against powdery mildews. The strobilurin currently on the market for grapes is Abound. There is another coming onto the market soon called Sovran and another several years away called Flint. They are not incredibly good stand-alone mildew materials, but they are very good in rotation programs or alternation programs with DMI compounds.

Fungicide Modes of Action

Mode of action is how the fungicide affects or kills the fungus. Sulfur compounds work by preventing spore germination. That is why it is very important that the sulfur compound get to the plant surface before the fungus does. Oil fungicides (e.g., Stylet oil, the Orchex oils) are contact fungicides that obliterate the fungus. You get your best activity when the mildew is already there. This is one class of compounds you could actually use to get a handle on mildew if it is getting out of control. The oils, like the sulfur fungicides, are not prone to resistance development.

STROBILURIN FUNGICIDES

Strobilurin fungicides work in two ways: 1) they prevent the spore germination process; and 2) they have some curative activity. They don't prevent the fungus from forming a germ tube, but they prevent the spore from actually getting established in the tissue. They can be absorbed by the leaves and burn out some of the infections. The companies that make them are not recommending them to be used in this latter fashion, because of the potential for resistance development. They should be incorporated as protectants. Therefore, the compound needs to be protecting the plant **before** the fungus gets there.

DMI FUNGICIDES

DMI fungicides have been our standard mildewcides for years. They actually have some curative activity. They hinder the infection process by interfering with the formation of cellular membranes. The DMIs and the strobilurins act on the fungus in different places and along different biochemical pathways. However, both classes are very site-specific. This means that they only affect the pathogenic fungus at one or two biochemical points, unlike the oils or the sulfurs. Because of this narrow specificity, they are prone to resistance. The strobilurin fungicides are a class of compounds that are going through the registration process quite quickly. Once we get these on the market, we need to use them wisely to keep them on the market—use fungicide resistance management strategies that will preserve them.

RESISTANCE TO DMI FUNGICIDES

A lot of work has been done with powdery mildews, DMI fungicides, and resistance. Resistance, or the loss of sensitivity to these compounds, is the norm if sound resistance management strategies are not followed. You can assume that populations of powdery mildew you have in your grapes now probably need more DMI fungicide to kill them than a population in the same vineyard needed ten years ago. This resistance, or loss of sensitivity, is a gradual process. It is not the kind of occurrence where one year the grower gets excellent control and the next year he or she goes out and has total control failures. It manifests itself to the grower or fieldperson as a gradual loss of control where you might just be saying to yourself, "This stuff doesn't seem to work like it used to."

You can overcome this gradual loss of sensitivity by spraying at tighter intervals (which becomes unaffordable sooner or later), or you can raise the spray application rates (you obviously cannot go off label). Therefore, once this starts to happen, the grower has a problem.

Resistance to the sterol inhibitors, again, occurs in small genetic steps and is a gradual loss of sensitivity. You probably remember the first year that you used some of these and thought that you had a silver bullet. At least in cherries, it was like the silver bullet. We didn't have any mildew problems for several years, and then we had several years of extremely high disease pressure. Reports started coming from growers that DMI materials didn't seem to work as well as they once did. Sooner or later, the loss of sensitivity to the fungicide gets to a point where it is affecting the field performance and the fungicide is not providing adequate control.

The key to it is to try to keep insensitivity from developing in the first place. How does this insensitivity to DMI fungicides develop? Let's go back to about 1982 and come forward through about 1989.

There were really three different types of propagules in the naturally occurring mildew fungus population. There were individuals that were very sensitive to low doses of the DMI fungicide (e.g., 2 ounces). There were individuals that were less sensitive to doses of DMI fungicide (e.g., 4 ounces), and then there were individuals that were sensitive only to high doses (e.g., up to 6 ounces in order to control).

As we used these compounds year after year, the propagules controlled by lower DMI rates were eliminated from the population. Seven years later, high rates were required to control the mildew, which consisted of propagules sensitive to only high rates of the fungicide. As time progresses, a high dose of DMI fungicide is required to control the disease.

Dr. Doug Gubler at the University of California, Davis, has shown that this sensitivity shift can actually occur within one season. For example, in 1995, disease pressure was very high. This fungus can reproduce every five days under pressure of that extreme.

There were millions of spores being produced. The sensitivity shift, where you go from a mixed population to an exclusively high-dose population, can occur within that growing season. The sensitivity shift can occur after four or five sprays using the same compound. You may have good control early, but later, the compound starts to slip.

FACTORS THAT AFFECT RESISTANCE RISK
The Nature of the Chemical

Any chemical that is systemic, site-specific, and has a narrow mode of action is more susceptible to resistance.

The Intensity and Type of Usage

It is recommended that you do not exceed three DMI applications per year, and that those applications are protective rather than eradicative in nature.

The Nature of the Pathogen Affects Resistance Development

The powdery mildews that reproduce fast and are spread through the air are more prone to develop resistance.

The Proportion of Naturally-Occurring Resistant Strains in the Population

RESISTANCE MANAGEMENT

The American Phytopathological Society has developed recommendations to manage fungicide resistance:

Mix or Alternate Compounds with Different Modes of Action (e.g., strobilurins and DMI, etc.)

The preferred way is alternations. Alternate compounds with different modes of action in the same season. For example, the DMI is alternated with a sulfur or alternated with an oil or a strobilurin.

Limit the Number of Sprays

It is generally thought that you are safe using three DMI or strobilurin applications per year or less.

The Timing of Application
(Very important)

Confine the use of a systemic fungicide, if you can, to early in the season to try to keep the epidemic from getting out of control in the first place. In doing so, you are going to be exposing a lot fewer individuals to that resistance-prone chemical. The fewer individual fungal propagules you expose to that chemical, the fewer that are going to be able to survive it. So, the early spray programs are quite critical.

Blocking

When using the strobilurins in rotation with other compounds, one should avoid using blocks of more than two consecutive strobilurin sprays. The break between strobilurin blocks should always be at least two sprays.

GOOD NEWS

There are some bright spots in our new chemistry. The newer strobilurins include Abound, Sovran, and Flint, and a number of experimental compounds. They fit well in alternations with the DMI fungicides. There is another class of compounds called quinolines.

The compound we have been looking at is called quinoxyfen, and it looks good for grape mildew control. These alternation programs provide excellent disease control and sound resistance management strategies. In our trials with alternations of DMI and strobilurins, we have obtained mildew control equal to that obtained with straight DMI or strobilurin compounds.

REFERENCES

Grape Pest Management, 1992. University of California Division of Agriculture and Natural Resources. University of California.

Pest Management

Mike Means
Viticulturist, Stimson Lane Vineyards and Estates
Grandview, Washington

Good pest management practices begin prior to planting a vineyard. The single most important of these is site selection. Aspects such as elevation, orientation, slope, air drainage, soil depth, soil uniformity, and availability of good water, must all be scrutinized closely. These aspects of the site will help determine what varieties to plant, what row orientation to use, the degree of ground preparation required, the need for frost protection, and other considerations.

Another major issue of site selection is crop history. Is the ground virgin or has it been planted to other crops? If the ground has been planted to other crops, do those crops harbor pests that could affect wine grapes? It may be necessary to fumigate the ground to reduce problems such as weed seed, nematodes, and disease-causing organisms such as verticillium.

Once the site evaluation has been completed and the varietal mix has been determined, it is essential to obtain plant material that is free of pests and disease organisms, such as phylloxera and viruses. Considering the life of a vineyard is 30-plus years, it is extremely important to obtain the best nursery stock on the market.

Certified plant material is available from numerous sources. Inquire about the source of all plant material you are considering for purchase and obtain proper documentation. Simple steps taken at this stage can help you avoid expensive problems in the future.

WHAT IS A PEST?

A pest is any organism that has a negative impact on our ability to produce the quantity and/or quality of fruit desired. Quality is the key to a prosperous industry!

THE PEST MANAGEMENT PROCESS

1. Know the pests that exist in your vineyard. It is essential to be able to identify pests and the damage they cause.
2. Implement a monitoring program that will allow you to track pest populations over time and evaluate pest damage.
3. Determine thresholds for various pests and damage levels attributed to those pests.
4. If thresholds are exceeded, apply the best strategies for controlling or reducing numbers below threshold levels.

Many resources are available to help new growers become familiar with these pests.

Over the years, our company has used a data sheet to record information on pest problems observed in the field. Most recently, we have started using hand-held computers which allow us to collect data while monitoring the vineyard. The data collected include: date, block, variety, and location within the block. Pest levels or counts, type and level of damage, and other visual observations are also recorded. After each monitoring session, data is downloaded, allowing us to track population levels over time and to maintain a historical record of problems. Three categories of pests are tracked—weeds, diseases, and insects and mites.

WEEDS

Weeds compete with vines for water and nutrients. Weed control is especially important in young plantings. Weeds can be controlled by cultivation or with the use of chemicals. Numerous implements have been developed to destroy weedy plants within the vine row. These devices can be very effective but are slow and, if not operated properly, can damage vines and trellis.

Chemical control of weeds is divided into two categories—residual herbicides and contact herbicides.

Residual herbicides are applied to the soil to prevent new weed growth. It is important to know the weed species that are present in each area to be treated and to select a residual herbicide that is effective against that spectrum of weeds.

Contact herbicides are nonselective and will kill or damage all green tissue they come in contact with. Care must be taken not to spray desirable foliage. Over the past few years, plant tubes have been developed to increase vine growth and protect young vines from herbicide sprays. These have been very helpful in reducing competition from weeds in the first year or two of vineyard establishment.

DISEASES

The two most important diseases that affect wine grapes in the state of Washington are powdery mildew and *Botrytis* bunch rot. Powdery mildew is the number one pest of wine grapes in the state. Sound cultural practices and an effective prophylactic chemical spray program are essential to prevent substantial losses due to this fungus. Cultural practices, including irrigation management that limits vine vigor and encourages an open canopy, help reduce the potential for infection. An open canopy aids sun infiltration, air movement, and spray penetration.

Numerous chemicals are available to help prevent mildew infections. It is extremely important to implement a program that incorporates materials with different modes of action in preventing powdery mildew. This approach is termed resistance management and is designed to extend the effective life of the materials we have to combat this disease.

Botrytis is another fungal disease that can cause severe damage under certain environmental conditions. Varieties with tight clusters are especially susceptible to this disease. Cultural practices similar to those discussed for mildew prevention should be employed. Pruning to minimize shoot congestion and some form of leaf (or shoot) removal to facilitate inner canopy drying are practices used to reduce the incidence of rot. Chemicals are available, but are limited in their efficacy in preventing this disease.

INSECTS AND MITES
Cutworms

These insects cause damage during the initial stage of growth (bud break) in the spring. The damage is caused by worms feeding on swelling buds and young shoots. To monitor this damage, count the number of buds that have been fed on. Each feeding site is called a strike. The object is to determine the number of strikes per vine. Thresholds at which controls needs to be applied are difficult to establish and depend on the level of insect population, level of damage, timing, weather, and other considerations. For cutworm, two strikes per vine should alert growers that sprays may be necessary.

Mealybugs

These insects move onto grape foliage and clusters in early spring. Damage is caused by the feeding insect excreting honeydew that covers foliage and fruit. Honeydew is an excellent growth medium for sooty mold that can affect fruit quality. Closely monitor leaves and clusters for signs of this pest. Mealybugs can be controlled by chemical application prior to bunch close.

Thrips

Thrips can be a problem throughout the season. Damage is done by thrips feeding on all green tissue. These insects can cause scarring on berries, shoots, and leaves. Severe scarring can lead to stunted shoots and berry shatter. Monitor leaves and clusters throughout the season for the presence of thrips. Thresholds can be developed by slapping shoot tips on a dark piece of paper and counting thrips per slap. Compare numbers of thrips to damage incurred to determine if control is necessary. Ten to twenty thrips per slap is the range at which growers should consider control measures. This pest can be controlled by chemical applications.

Leafhoppers

Leafhopper populations build over the entire growing season. Damage is caused by nymphs and adults sucking chlorophyll out of the leaves. Feeding reduces the photosynthetic output of the plant, which can lead to delayed ripening and defoliation. Monitor the number of nymphs per leaf. Select different leaves within the canopy depending on the time of year. The threshold for spraying should be set when growers find five to ten nymphs per leaf during the first brood and ten to twenty per leaf during the second brood. Control with chemical application.

Mites

Mites are more of a problem in hot, dry years. Vineyards under drip irrigation are more likely to be affected. Damage is done by the mites feeding on leaves, which reduces the photosynthetic output of the vine. Extreme damage can lead to delayed ripening and defoliation. Monitor the number of mites per leaf or the percentage of leaves infested. Control through chemical application.

WHAT CAN YOU DO TO MINIMIZE PEST PROBLEMS?

Select a site that receives adequate heat units. This will assure early ripening and strong vine growth. Healthy vines can tolerate higher populations of pests than weak vines. Select nursery stock that is free of disease and insect pests. Adopt sound cultural practices that reduce canopy congestion and encourage moderate vine vigor. Encourage beneficial organisms whenever possible. When chemical intervention is required, use materials that preserve beneficial insects and mites. When using chemicals, always follow label instructions, and use proper rates and calibration. Implement a chemical program that incorporates resistance management.

Critical Temperatures for Concord Grapes

APPENDIX

Preliminary research has given some rough estimates of what temperatures would be expected to kill primary buds. As the buds become active, swell, open, and begin growth, they become more susceptible to frost injury. Also, in any vineyard, there are some buds which are more susceptible or resistant than others to low temperatures. These are expressed as T-10, temperatures likely to kill 10 percent of the primary buds, and T-90, temperatures which are estimated to kill 90 percent of the primaries.

The values shown in the table below were determined in the laboratory and have not been checked extensively against field injury. Further, the test procedures were modified in 1997, and therefore, the data represent only one season's experience. In spite of these limitations, these values are distributed as a guide of what might be expected on cold nights. These estimates also provide a basis to which growers can relate their experiences of field injury.

CRITICAL TEMPERATURES*

Stage of Development	Definition	T-10	T-90
Dormant	Closed buds, inactive.	Variable	Subzero
First swell	Buds increase in size; scales separate to show brown, fussy young leaf tissue.	13	-3
Full swell	Buds swell further; young leaves become pink. Still closed around growing point.	21	10
Bud burst	Young leaves separate at tip to show the growing point.	25	16
1st leaf	First leaf is out of the bud, makes right angle with stem.	27	21
2nd leaf	Second leaf makes right angle with stem.	28	22
3rd leaf		28	26
4th leaf		28	27
5th leaf		28	27

*Critical temperatures for 10% (T-10) and 90% (T-90) kill of primary buds.

Chapter 16-481 WAC*
Grape Phylloxera Quarantine

APPENDIX

WAC 16-481-010
Establishing Quarantine

Grape phylloxera [*Daktulosphaira vitifoliae* (Fitch)] is an insect pest injurious to grape plants that can cause severe reductions in grape yield and ultimately the death of the grape plant. This pest is widely distributed throughout the United States and the world. Introductions of the pest into the state of Washington through infested grape plants, rootstock, and plant cuttings, or on contaminated grape cultivation or harvesting equipment could have a severe economic impact on the Washington grape industry. To prevent this, the director, under the authority provided in chapters 17.24 and 15.13 RCW, has established a quarantine to prevent the introduction of this pest into the state.

WAC 16-481-015
Definitions

(1) "Pest" means the insect of the order Homoptera and family Phylloxeridae, grape phylloxera [*Daktulosphaira vitifoliae* (Fitch)].

(2) "Infested area" means all states and territories of the United States and all areas outside the United States.

(3) "Area known to be free of grape phylloxera" means a specific property of a person or firm or a specific nursery stock growing ground surveyed by the department of agriculture of the shipping state.

(4) "Department" means the Washington State Department of Agriculture.

(5) "Director" means the director of the Washington State Department of Agriculture or the director's authorized representative.

(6) "Hardwood cutting" means a cutting from a grape plant taken during the period of dormancy and not including portions of the trunk of the plant produced during previous growing seasons.

(7) "Softwood cutting" means any cutting taken when the grape plant is not fully dormant.

(8) "Susceptible varieties" means grape plants that may serve as host to grape phylloxera and which show symptoms of decline when infested.

(9) "Nonsusceptible varieties" means grape plants that may serve as host to grape phylloxera but which do not show symptoms of decline when infested. Nonsusceptible varieties include Concord varieties and *V. vinifera* varieties on resistant rootstock.

WAC 16-481-025
Regulated Products

Products regulated under the grape phylloxera quarantine include:

(1) All grape plants, rootstock, and softwood cuttings, rooted or not. Hardwood cuttings meeting the definition in WAC 16-481-016(6) and dried grape vines used for ornamental purposes are exempt from the requirements in this chapter.

(2) All equipment that has been used for the cultivation or harvesting of grapes in a quarantine area.

(Continued)

---

*Washington Administrative Code

WAC 16-481-030
Conditions Governing Shipments—External

(1) Each shipment of grape plants, grape rootstock, and/or softwood cuttings from an infested area must be accompanied by a certificate signed by a duly authorized inspector of the department of agriculture of the state of origin of the shipment, or by a duly authorized inspector of the United States Department of Agriculture, Animal and Plant Health Inspection Service, stating that:

(a) The grape plants, rootstock, and/or softwood cuttings were grown in and shipped from an area known to be free from grape phylloxera; or

(b) The grape plants, rootstock, or softwood cuttings were grown under an approved sterile media system; or

(c) For small shipments (five hundred articles or less), softwood cuttings were carefully inspected by an authorized inspector and were found to be free from grape phylloxera; or

(d) The grape plants, rootstock, and/or softwood cuttings were subject to one of the two treatments outlined in subsection (2) of this section or such additional methods as may be determined to be effective and are approved in writing by the director and were stored in a manner after treatment that would prevent reinfestation.

(2) Acceptable treatments shall include:

(a) Hot water treatment. Dormant, rooted grape plants or rootstock shall be washed to remove all soil or other propagative media. Dormant rooted plants or rootstock shall be immersed in a hot water bath for a period of not less than three minutes nor more than five minutes at a temperature of not less than 125 degrees F. (52 degrees C.) nor more than 130 degrees F. (55 degrees C.) at any time during immersion; or

(b) Methyl bromide fumigation. Grape plants, rootstock, or softwood cuttings may be treated by methyl bromide fumigation. Fumigation shall be in an approved gas-tight fumigation chamber, equipped with a heating unit, fan for dispersal of gas and clearing the chamber of gas after fumigation, and interior ther-mometer readable from the outside. Fumigation shall be with a dosage of two pounds (0.908 kg.) of methyl bromide per one thousand cubic feet (twenty-eight cubic meters) for a period of three hours at a temperature of between 65 degrees F. (18.3 degrees C.) and 70 degrees F. (21.1 degrees C.). The fan shall be operated for a period of ten minutes after the injection of the gas.

(3) All shipments of grape plants, rootstock, and/or softwood cuttings from an infested area shall be plainly marked with the contents on the outside of the package or container as "grape plants," "grape rootstock," or "grape cuttings."

(4) Notification requirements of WAC 16-481-060 are met.

WAC 16-481-050
Equipment Cleaning Requirements

(1) All equipment used for cultivation or harvesting of grapes in grape phylloxera quarantine areas outside the state or infested properties within the state must be thoroughly washed or steam cleaned to remove all soil and plant material prior to entry into the state of Washington. Such equipment shall be subject to inspection by authorized inspectors of the department of agriculture.

(2) Any equipment found to be in violation of the sanitation requirement shall be subject to detention by the department until such equipment is thoroughly cleaned at the expense of the owner or shipper, or provision made to transport the equipment directly out of the state.

WAC 16-481-060
Notification Requirements

The plant services division of the department of agriculture shall be notified by United States mail or telefax prior to the shipment of grape plants and/or cuttings under the grape phylloxera quarantine into this state from an infested area. Such notice shall include, but not be limited to, the approximate number of the grape plants, rootstock, and/or softwood cuttings; the shipper; the consignee; the method of treatment used, if applicable; and the approximate date of delivery.

WAC 16-481-070
Disposition of Products Shipped in Violation of This Quarantine— Violations

Any shipment of grape plants, rootstock, and/or softwood cuttings shipped into or entering the state of Washington from an infested area and not accompanied by the required certificate and/or not complying with the notice requirement in WAC 16-481-060, shall be returned to point of origin, or destroyed at the option and expense of the owner or owners, or their responsible agent or agents.

WAC 16-481-075
Violations—Penalties

Any person who violates the terms of the grape phylloxera quarantine may be subject to a criminal or civil penalty, as determined by the director, in an amount not more than five thousand dollars for each violation. Every person who, through an act of commission or omission, procures, aids, or abets in the violation, shall be considered to have violated this chapter and may be subject to criminal or civil penalty.

Chapter 16-483 WAC*
Grape Virus Quarantine

APPENDIX

WAC 16-483-001
Establishing Quarantine

The production of wine grapes, table grapes, and grape plant nursery stock are important industries in the state of Washington. The director has determined that these industries are threatened by the introduction of the virus diseases known as leafroll, fanleaf, corky bark, and stem pitting that are not established in the state of Washington. The presence of these virus diseases cannot be determined by the most rigorous visual examination of dormant grape plants or propagative parts of grape plants. Introductions of these virus diseases would entail great economic loss to the horticultural industries of the state. To prevent this harm, the director, under the authority provided in chapter 17.24 RCW, has established a quarantine setting forth rules for the importation of grape planting stock into the state of Washington.

WAC 16-483-005
Definitions

(1) "Department" means the Washington State Department of Agriculture.

(2) "Director" means the director of the Washington State Department of Agriculture or the director's authorized representative.

(3) "Grape plants and propagative parts" means live plants, hardwood cuttings, softwood cuttings, rootstocks, and any other parts of the grape plant (*Vitis* species), except fruit, capable of propagation.

(4) "Official certificate" means a document issued by an official inspection agency including but not limited to phytosanitary certificates, inspection certificates, or other letters, tags, stamps, or similar documents certifying plant quality or condition.

WAC 16-483-010
Quarantine Area

Areas under quarantine for grape virus include all states and territories of the United States outside of the territorial borders of the state of Washington.

WAC 16-483-020
Regulated Articles

All plants and plant parts capable of propagation (except fruit) of grapes are regulated under the terms of the grape virus quarantine.

WAC 16-483-030
Regulations

Grape plants and propagative parts will be admitted into the state of Washington provided the following provisions are complied with:

(1) The grape plants or propagative parts have been certified in accordance with the regulations of an official state agency, which certification program includes inspection and testing by indexing on suitable indicator hosts for fanleaf, leafroll, stem pitting, and corky bark virus diseases. All shipments of such grape cuttings shall be accompanied by a certificate issued by an agency of the state of origin, certifying that the grape plants or cuttings were produced under official certification regulations and meet official certification standards as to freedom from fanleaf, leafroll, stem pitting, and corky bark virus diseases.

(2) All shipments of grape nursery stock

shall be plainly marked with the contents on the outside of the package or container.

(3) Persons shipping or transporting regulated articles, identified in WAC 16-483-020, into this state from areas under quarantine shall notify the department's plant protection branch by United States mail or telefax, prior to shipment, of the nature and the quantity of each shipment, the expected date of arrival at destination, the name of the intended receiver, and the destination. The person to whom the articles are shipped shall hold the same until they are inspected and/or released by the department.

WAC 16-483-040
Disposition of Material
Shipped in Violation

All grape plants or parts thereof arriving in the state of Washington in violation of the provisions of the grape virus quarantine, shall be refused admittance into the state of Wash-ington, or shall be immediately sent out of the state or destroyed at the option and expense of the owner or owners, or their responsible agents.

WAC 16-483-050
Exemption

The restrictions on the movement of regulated articles set forth in this chapter shall not apply to grape plants or propagative parts imported for experimental or trial purposes by the United States Department of Agriculture and the state experiment stations in the state of Washington, provided that a permit to import is issued by the director of agriculture.

WAC 16-483-060
Violation—Penalty

All violations of the grape virus quarantine shall be punishable by the criminal and/or civil penalties provided by law.

---

*Washington Administrative Code

Glossary

Basal Bud—a small bud that lies at the base of a cane or spur, which usually does not grow unless the distal buds fail to grow.

Bilateral Cordon—vine training in which the trunk(s) is divided into two branches extended horizontally on a supporting wire; often referred to as cordon training.

Blackleaf—a physiological disease of grapevines causing brown or black pigmentation in the leaf and accompanied by reduced photosynthesis capacity. Blackleaf is usually associated with high light intensity, heavy crops, and water stress.

Brix—the scale used to measure soluble solids or sugar in grapes; roughly equivalent to percent.

Caliche—a layer of soil composed of minerals that results in poor water drainage and constricted plant root distribution.

Canes—current or most recent season's stem growth.

Canopy—the layers of leaves produced by grapevines.

Certified Planting Stock—grapevine propagation material certified free of known virus diseases and insects by the Washington State Department of Agriculture, under regulations of the Grapevine Certification Program.

Chlorosis—yellowing or blanching of green portions of a plant, particularly the leaves, which can result from nutrient deficiencies, cold wet soil, diseases, or other factors.

Clone—a group of vines of a uniform type, propagated vegetatively from an original mother vine.

Cordon—Permanent arm of the grapevine.

Cover Crops—grass or other plant material grown between the grapevine rows.

Critical Temperature—the temperature at which buds or other plant tissues will freeze and die.

Cutting—a severed portion of a cane used for propagation.

Diurnal Temperature—temperature variation during a 24-hour period.

Head Training System—a system that uses a permanent trunk to support canes and spurs but has no permanent arms.

Heat Units—the measure of accumulated heat through the growing season. Daily heat units are obtained by averaging the maximum and minimum temperature and subtracting 50°F.

Internode—that portion of a shoot or cane between two adjacent nodes.

Lateral—a branch of the main axis of the cluster; also a shoot arising from the main shoot.

Must—crushed berries and juice.

Phylloxera—a small, yellowish, aphidlike insect that attacks roots and/or leaves.

Rachis—berry cluster stem.

Shoot—current season's stem growth that bears leaves and buds.

Shot Berry—very small berries that fail to develop to normal size; usually seedless.

Spur—the cane after being shortened by pruning; usually two to five nodes long.

Sucker—a shoot arising from the lower part of the trunk, or from the part of the stem below the ground.

Veraison—the stage of development when berries begin to soften and/or color.

Water Sprouts—rapidly growing shoots arising from latent buds on branches or trunks.